EDINBURGH UNIVERSITY PUBLICATIONS

HISTORY PHILOSOPHY AND ECONOMICS

II

Studies in the
HISTORY AND METHODS
OF THE SCIENCES

★

ARTHUR DAVID RITCHIE

EDINBURGH
The University Press
1958

© 1958

THE EDINBURGH UNIVERSITY PRESS
Agents
THOMAS NELSON AND SONS LTD
Parkside Works Edinburgh 9
36 Park Street London W1
312 Flinders Street Melbourne C1
302-304 Barclays Bank Building Commissioner and Kruis Streets Johannesburg

THOMAS NELSON AND SONS (CANADA) LTD
91-93 Wellington Street West Toronto 1

THOMAS NELSON AND SONS
19 East 47th Street New York 17

SOCIÉTÉ FRANÇAISE D'ÉDITIONS NELSON
97 rue Monge Paris Vᵉ

PRINTED IN GREAT BRITAIN
BY OLIVER AND BOYD LTD., EDINBURGH

CONTENTS

v

Contents

CHAPTER I

INTRODUCTION

Sciences, not science · General aims of this book · Summary of principles

§1. THESE studies are bound to appear incomplete and patchy, and for such defects excuses can be made, even if there are none for other defects. No science is complete, none has solved all its problems, surveyed its whole subject matter, or even discovered its limitations ; though limitations it must have, for it deals with some problems better than others. Each claims to say the first word on its own special topics, and rightly. Rightly too, for its own immediate purpose, it dismisses many other topics as irrelevant. Sometimes it can be seen that a science has said the last word on certain special and restricted topics, but last words in general do not belong to science, and as long as human experience is incomplete no human being utters any completely last words. This may perhaps suffice as an apology for incompleteness.

If the sciences are patchy, as they clearly are, that does not in itself excuse patchiness in discussing them. Yet it has to be my excuse. The sciences have arisen out of certain special human relations (briefly considered in Chapter II) and consist of special human practices and thought about the practice. They have grown, developed and sometimes changed radically in the process. The whole of any branch of science is the whole of that historical process as a part of human experience, and nobody can write its biography in full any more than he can write any man's biography in full. Yet we cannot understand what a science is now unless we understand how it has come to be what it is, that is to say historically. The only alternative is to take it *a priori* as we suppose it might be, or ought to be, or will be if people take our advice about it. Since our historical survey cannot be a full one we must use the sampling method and our choice of samples depends upon our purpose or bias or philosophical point of view, whichever you prefer to call it. At any rate, positivists write one kind of history of science and bring out certain important

[1]

points while ignoring others. Marxists write another kind of history, devised for purposes of political propaganda, as they themselves say in their more candid moments. Anybody who wants to know what kind of philosophical axe I am grinding is referred to §§2 and 3 of this chapter and to the concluding chapter.

I have spoken of the sciences in the plural, not only because they are manifestly plural but even more because singular SCIENCE is the Sacred Cow of 20th century idolatry, from which the worshipper procures his magical milk (sweet or sour) and other magical bovine products. One of these is SCIENTIFIC METHOD. A man who has successfully carried out one or two investigations of a specialist character thinks that he is thereby entitled to pontificate about things in general. The illusion is not entirely new. Socrates discovered something very like it in 5th century Athens. But it is more widespread and more dangerous now than in his day, and among Athenians whose sense of the ridiculous was well developed.

There are, however, subtle and insidious forms of this illusion that flourish because scientific modes of reasoning are most powerful and precise when dealing with the most abstract topics. The most abstract are also the most specialized, yet not the most specifically informative topics. Many, even very acute thinkers, have been led to suppose that the methods of mathematics *by themselves* or the methods of physics *by themselves* can do almost everything almost at once. To work out the balance sheet of a Company the abstract and universal laws of arithmetic are used and very little else, and the information given is specialized, though useful within its limits. It does not tell you how to deal with complaints about the food in the works canteen, how to cut down fuel consumption or pilfering from the stores, or whether the Managing Director really needs two new cars for his own use. Yet all these things have a bearing on the balance sheet.

Many writers have emphasized the tentative character of most scientific reasoning and even claimed a kind of moral superiority for tentativeness, which they take to be opposed to dogmatism and absolutism. Precipitate judgment, where evidence is not complete and immediate judgment is not required, is wrong, as Descartes said long ago. Where action is purely exploratory, tentative action is often possible and is right. But more often action calls for definite judgment and tentative action is bungled action. Anybody who tries to dive into the sea tentatively will find it a painful or at best a disappointing experience. To come back to the sciences : a great deal of theorizing is makeshift or speculative ; it is put forward in order to be knocked about and altered. There is no progress without this kind of theorizing ; it is conspicuous and constantly discussed. There is another kind of theory which is unobtrusive and seldom discussed, once it has been put forward, which is not tentative and may even be final, but limited in scope and always closely linked to practice. Because of this there are such events in scientific history as classical researches ; work on which all subsequent developments are built and from which nothing has to be taken away later ; work which is fundamental, convincing, complete within its limits.

Unfortunately, there are not many classical researches and outside the most abstract sciences very few indeed. Dr. J. B. Conant (*On Understanding Science*, 1947) shows very well how to use them. He discusses, for example, Torricelli's Experiment, the invention of the barometer (to put the matter briefly). Since Empedocles demonstrated the fundamental fact that there are gases, that so-called empty space is not so empty as it looks, very little more was done till Torricelli (1643). What he did was simple, decisive, immensely fertile for practice and theory ; for methods of handling gases, for examining their properties, for the theory of the gaseous state. Once the observations were made, and the obvious deductions from them, something was established from which further work and speculation could proceed. Nobody has revised, corrected, much less contradicted anything. While we praise Torricelli and his colleague Viviani we must not forget the Italian glassworkers who provided them with strong, tough, straight, clear glass tubes for their experiments. Empedocles and Aristotle had nothing of the sort available, and for them such experiments were impossible and unimaginable.

Newton's work on the spectral colours is another classical

research, showing for the first time that a glass prism is not just a toy but the physicist's most powerful analytical tool, and making the first step towards the theory of light (cf. *Newton and the Origin of Colours* by M. Roberts and E. R. Thomas, 1934). On the other hand, Dalton's work on the atomic theory was fundamental but not quite classical, it was not complete and left loose ends which were not tied up for half a century (see Chapter VII, §8).

In biology Pasteur's disproof of the theory of spontaneous generation was strictly classical (see Chapter VIII, §3). In contrast Mendel's work on heredity was not quite classical, some of its loose ends still look just as loose as when it was first rescued from oblivion early this century.

The Greeks were good at classical researches and enjoyed the advantage of having no predecessors. I shall make use of three of them (Chapters III, IV and VI). Nobody will doubt that the work of Archimedes on *Floating Bodies* is classical. Some, however, may shake their heads over Aristarchus on *Sizes and Distances of the Sun and Moon*, since the first precise measurements of the sun's distance were not published till 1941, and not arrived at by his methods. There may be even more shaking of heads over Euclid's *Elements* ; a mere textbook, mostly a compilation of the work of others, and of course quite out of date.

The advantage of the classical research for my purpose is that it shows up that aspect of scientific practice and theory (rare though it is) where truth can be said to shine by its own light, and where a successful metaphysical leap has been achieved. Mostly we see only fitful gleams of light, which do little more than show up the surrounding fog. A classical research can at once disperse the fog. More often fog disperses very slowly and in patches, as happened when the old alchemy began to give way to chemistry (Chapter VII). There have been bogus sciences, and we must not suppose they all belong to past history. This must be my excuse for the rest of the book and its miscellaneous character. I cannot claim to be comprehensive, but have tried to look around a bit. Above all I have tried to avoid the common error of supposing that physics is the one and only science and that all other studies just creep in as hangers-on or else are not scientific at all. It is one of the ironies of history that Newton himself saw clearly that his system was in no way complete, yet nearly all his successors thought it was, that in general and in principle he had solved all problems, leaving only various details to be worked out by using known methods.

§2. If asked to state my general aim, the only simple reply available is that it is to illustrate two well known sayings of Kant :—' Thoughts without content are empty, intuitions without concepts are blind.' ' Reason has insight only into that which it produces after a plan of its own.' The second of these is an afterthought appearing first in the Preface to the Second Edition of the *Critique of Pure Reason*, never fully worked out or applied, though the ' plans ' are the work of the *imagination* and involve the *schemata*, which he does discuss (A,137, B,176.). The first and most important dictum he drops when he comes to his moral theory. Kant was rightly jealous for the autonomy of moral judgment, but he had no need to empty Practical Reason for that purpose. Theoretical Reason also needs its own kind of autonomy and possesses it in the imagination. These criticisms, however, are incidental, Kant makes his fundamental point clear enough ; thought and experience and their subjective and objective aspects must be distinguished but never separated. Even so Kant did not entirely rid himself of the consequences of Hume's gravest error. Hume was not only a *phenomenalist* but a *visualist*. (Cf. H. H. Price, *Touch and Organic Sensation* (*Proc. Arist. Soc.*), 1943-44, p. i.) In spite of this diagnosis of the disease and the simple remedy for it, the visualist epidemic continues (see Appendix). Experience for him is passive visual recipience, imagination is an echo of it or else is fiction and totally false, thought is an *ignis fatuus*. He failed to notice that primary experience is, as Berkeley said in *The New Theory of Vision* (if not, alas, elsewhere), that of grasping and handling and being mutually involved in things. We are both active and passive, and vision becomes genuine experience, not just a play of lights and colours, only if it is involved in the realm of interaction, to which it stands as a set of external signs.

[5]

Kant comes pretty near to stating that the ' facts ' of the mathematical and experimental sciences are all artifacts, which does not mean that they are false in any way, but that they are the results of mechanical manipulation. If an artifact successfully fulfils its purpose it must be genuinely constructed out of genuine stuff, the technical or pragmatic criterion of truth. It follows that the theories of the sciences contain imaginative constructions or models derived by analogy, from mechanical manipulation ; and liable to distortion if taken visually, for visual imagination has no criteria of its own (see Appendix).

All this creates difficulties when we come to study the organic realm. We can go some way by using experimental methods with living things, treating them as though artificial. In many respects they are very like artifacts, and that is not surprising since we are living organisms and our artifacts are of our own making. For all that, living organisms are not artifacts, hence we find them difficult to understand. Hence comes a greater difficulty in studying human beings, when the artificer becomes his own artifact, or perhaps *vice versa*.

§3. It may be well to summarize certain other points, which can be ranked as conclusions or else as premisses, and which I hope to illustrate and amplify.

(i) There are no hard, atomic, pure or mere facts. Everything factual is such because it belongs to a system bound together by theory. For all that, new facts may be intrusive and cause theoretical disturbances.

(ii) It is the illusion of the visualist that he can observe completely objectively, like a spectator who is not a performer in the game. In the *haptic* realm as opposed to the *scopic* (see Appendix for a further account of these terms) whatever pushes is also pushed, as Newton pointed out. An object is objective in virtue of being handled by a subject. Every judgment about an object is the *arbitrium* of a subject, and so far arbitrary. Again, so far as it is made public it has to use the conventions of that public.

(iii) In consequence of (i), notwithstanding (ii), we have to presuppose one universal Public Space, the matrix of all

[6]

processes that are externally related, connected or separated as *partes extra partes*. The human body is one of these *partes*, though in one respect a peculiar one, since the consciousness and will (mind, soul, or spirit) of each one of us operates through the body of each one of us.

(iv) Notwithstanding the predominance of space, the paradigm or model type of fact is not the desiccated, artificial fact of the experimental sciences which cannot exist outside the laboratory but a more robust if less precise kind of fact, the evidence of the lawyer or historian. This is an affirmation by a person or subject to other persons or subjects about relations between them (see Chapter IX). All public scientific facts depend on these prior affirmations.

(v) No study can be reckoned fully scientific until it has undergone the Ordeal by Quackery, whether painless and quick as for Greek mathematics or painful and long as for chemistry.

(vi) Science is first a way of doing certain special things, a technique, and next a way of thinking about these special things and not others. There is no one universal scientific method, any more than there is one universal method of catching fish. Each fish has to be caught by a method appropriate to that fish in those circumstances in which it is to be found. Those who ignore this limitation do not catch the fish. A technique does not need to claim infallibility, but frequent failure is a broad hint to look for a better.

Each successful technique has solved its own inductive problem of how to arrive at a general conclusion from a limited set of particular observations. One successful technique does not by itself produce another successful technique, even if it provides useful hints ; the right way to catch sharks is not the right way to catch herrings, or sand eels. The working scientist is hardly aware of the problems that philosophers have discussed since Hume set them off. When he has got his apparatus to work after repeated failures, he has probably been applying Mill's canons ; but he has, very sensibly, been thinking about his apparatus not about his methods of thinking. This is not to say that there is no inductive problem, but that there are two. There is the technician's problem : *solvitur* *laborando,* in the drawing office, laboratory, workshop or in the field. For the purpose of his labours he presupposes that some things only are relevant, and all others irrelevant. He thus leaves to the metaphysicians their cosmological problem —either the universe is as Hume supposed and no one change is relevant to any other change, or else it is as Leibniz supposed and no one part can be changed without changing all other parts, so that nothing is irrelevant to anything else. In other words, the Humean universe is so empty and loose that experiment is useless and tells us nothing ; the Leibnizian is so full and close knit that experiment is impossible or else tells us nothing we do not know already. Can we specify an intermediate or compromise universe ? *

(vii) The most precise, communicable and systematic of general assertions that can be made about the world are chrono-topo-graphical, if I may be allowed to use the term. Spatiotemporal order is the minimum required to construct a world of things that can be handled and measured. Recognizing this Galileo and Descartes emphasized what they considered the Primary Qualities of Bodies and exalted them over the Secondary. Berkeley extended the arguments of Descartes and Newton to reach the conclusion, in *De Motu,* that physical science could and should be pure kinematics, pure chrono-topo-graphical theory. Ernst Mach said the same in the late 19th century. Perhaps one should remember Hobbes' attempt to define Euclidean figures in kinematic terms. The arguments of logical positivists of the 20th century about *meaningfulness* and *verifiability,* when stripped of verbiage, come to much the same.

The practice of working physicists has never quite kept within the bounds assigned to them by reductionist critics. Physicists include even in their abstract theory entities not purely chrono-topo-graphical. Moreover no generalization is strictly verifiable or even falsifiable, because any hypothesis can be upheld by introducing sufficient subsidiary hypotheses or by taking a sufficiently narrow view of the facts.

---

* I was confused about induction in my *Scientific Method* (1923). But there are some corrections in *Logic of Question and Answer* (*Essays in Philosophy,* 1947) and in *Science and Politics* (Riddell Lectures, 1947).

(viii) Even in mathematics and physics we do not entirely escape the normal criteria of human judgment, which are æsthetic, moral and technical (or pragmatic). Thus the human reactions to a baby crying may be considered under these three heads : ' That is an unpleasant noise.' ' Ought I to do anything for the child ? ' ' How can I intervene successfully ? ' The theoretical physicist proceeds as though the moral and technical issues have all in principle been decided for him and in his favour ; that he is doing as he ought (whatever it may be) and is capable of doing it successfully (whatever it may be). The criteria of his conscious and operative judgments are æsthetic. These limitations do no harm if the physicist is ' pure ' enough and may even be useful. For the technologist or ' applied ' physicist they are dangerous. He ought before he acts to ask himself the questions : ' By what right do I interfere ? ', ' Do I understand the consequences of my action ? '

(ix) The various sciences have arisen as distinct, autonomous disciplines and should not be confused ; but their subject matters are interrelated. There are important relations between chemical and living processes, between animal and human behaviour, between the human and cosmic realms.

CHAPTER II

PRE-SCIENTIFIC AND SCIENTIFIC

Rudiments of science · Pre-scientific not always wrong nor post-scientific always right · The Greek contribution · Difficulties of observation · Experimental method

§1. THOUGH the sciences are many, there is justification for their common name ; just as languages are many and very different yet all linguistic. Thus some preliminary general remarks are necessary. Human activities in order to be rated as scientific must at least be systematic, critical, exploratory and speculative. Theories have to be excogitated, but out of something not nothing ; out of techniques practised with some success and in their own right.

The scientific way of *thinking* in any manifest form is relatively new in human history. So far as the natural sciences and mathematics are concerned, it goes back no further than two millennia and a half. It is not yet completely assimilated or understood. As opposed to the scientific way of *thinking*, the scientific way of *acting*, or some part of it, is as old as mankind, and man's immemorial folk-lore. The first signs of human life discovered by archæologists are tools or indications of the use of them. Some rudiments of tool using are observed among animals, specially birds and mammals, but no animal deliberately makes tools for the purpose of making other tools. That act is specifically human. It marks the beginning of all the practical arts or techniques by which men obtain the means of life. It is also the beginning of that kind of practice which leads to science, though science itself is more than practice. All the genuine sciences arise out of useful arts ; mathematics from the calculations and measurements used in marketing, land surveying and planning buildings ; physics from the handling of materials for use and all working with material tools ; biology from the techniques of the hunter, fisherman, farmer, and the treatment of disease ; and so on. A complete list of useful arts or techniques would have to find room for the most ingenious tools of all, the tools of language, spoken and written ; and it would have to include the arts of law and government. There are grounds for claiming that the first rudiments of science proper developed from these last and that mathematics and physics do not have the seniority commonly assigned to them.

The practical arts are not sciences as long as they are pursued solely for utility. Science begins when utility is abandoned temporarily for the sake of understanding, in order to develop theory. The first beginnings of science are rightly attributed to the Greeks, and to no others, because they made this change. In this connection it is irrelevant to ask whether Greek technique was superior or not to that of neighbouring peoples or how much of their technique was borrowed. They were enterprising and acquisitive and doubtless borrowed all they could ; but science was not there to borrow and they had to invent it for themselves.

A motive is needed to initiate scientific enquiry, usually said to be curiosity or wonder ; and so it is, but of a special sort. A dog sniffing around a lamp-post exhibits curiosity, perhaps even wonder, but there is nothing very scientific about his enquiries ; nothing very much except habit. Men are creatures of habit, like dogs, though less content with mere habit. Scientific curiosity may grow out of technique, when it is found to be partially but not entirely successful ; out of general observation, when natural processes are found to be partially orderly, not completely. Mere impotence or mere chaos produce no response. Complete success or contemplation of complete order would produce no positive response either. It is the mixture of success and failure, or order and disorder that is stimulating. Theory begins either by taking ordinary general concepts, and giving them a technical twist, or by taking the almost unconscious concepts imbedded in technical practices, liberating and generalizing them.

Theory, which is the fruit of understanding, generally gives rise to improved practice in the long run, to what is conveniently called technology ; but sometimes only in the very long run and not necessarily then. Astronomical theory about bodies outside the solar system has not yet had any practical application, and it is to be hoped it never will. On

B   [11]

the other side pure technics, pure trial and error without any theory, may succeed as far as success is possible. Technique, the use and design of tools, is almost automatically self improving—up to a point. Up to a point the intelligent apprentice can do better than his master simply by trying. After a time the process of improvement slows down and tends to come to an end. The sticking point is usually far short of perfection ; then improved understanding from scientific theory can help. But not always. If you wish to build in stone and use the post and lintel type of design, you cannot do better * than the Greeks of the 5th century B.C. If you wish to build in stone using the arch, you cannot do better * than the medieval builders. Whatever can be done in stone has been done, and done without help from science.

A more striking case is that of musical instruments, most of which developed by pure technics without the help of theory. In particular, the violin makers of Cremona in the early 18th century attained perfection (apparently) in design and materials. Violin makers ever since have just imitated them. The physical theory of sound has suggested no change in design, and modern technology of materials no important change in materials, so far.

These examples are out of the ordinary run. Usually, practice uninspired by scientific theory stagnates at a stage where the thing is worth doing, but not half so well done as it might be. In the domain of medicine and agriculture this is clearly seen. The practice of both improved enormously after the mid 19th century, when fundamental scientific theory about living organisms, their conditions of life, growth and reproduction, and their relation to their environment at last became available, and also scientific methods of examining the facts of each particular case, methods of diagnosis. For without theory there are no reliable methods of diagnosis, and without proper diagnosis no sound methods of treatment. Earlier people could see something was wrong ; they could not see what was wrong. Agriculture and medicine are specially good examples, because for at least a century earlier they had been just about as progressive as was possible along the lines of

* To say ' better ' technically is safe enough. To say ' better ' artistically is more risky but worth risking.

pure technics, of commonsense and trial and error. These had done much, enough to make it clear how much more could not be done yet. In the first half of the 19th century nobody yet knew how to deal with infectious diseases, apart from smallpox, and nobody yet knew how to deal with the exhaustion of the soils of Western Europe after centuries of cultivation by traditional methods.*

§2. It is customary to contrast scientific with pre-scientific or non-scientific ways of thought in order to show that the former are all purity and light, the latter all darkness and superstition. But those who brag most loudly of their own scientific purity of thought cling most passionately to their own kind of super- stition, their special fables, magic and witchcraft. To avoid libel it is safest to refer to the 19th century for examples ; Auguste Comte and Herbert Spencer will do.†

It is easy by quoting a few of the stupidest samples of pre- scientific thought that can be found to make it out intrinsically silly. But that game is not a scientific one, and it can be played effectively against the self-appointed champions of science as well as against anybody else. Consider, for example, the medical profession. A few medical men are charlatans ; some, though honest, are not very competent and make a good many mistakes ; even the best make mistakes sometimes. If the whole of our evidence is to be on these lines we can make short work of the claims of medicine ; obviously it is super- stition and fraud, and the medical profession should be liqui- dated. On the other hand we may look only at the best the best practitioners do and then we must conclude that, though they are a little lower than the angels, the difference is negligible. We can try to strike an average and base a judgment on that, but it is difficult. Even under the most favourable conditions

* It is important to distinguish between pure science and technology, since their aims are different ; but equally to remember that neither flourishes in isolation. The difference is just that one uses techné for the sake of logos, the other logos for the sake of techné.

† Spencer's *a priori* definition of evolution as change from the unstable, homo- geneous to the stable, heterogeneous is bad metaphysics and also fiction—it does not happen. Comte's religion of humanity is a sillier superstition than that of any heathen in his blindness who bows to wood and stone. At least the wood and stone are genuine.

[13]

averages are abstractions of doubtful significance, and where we are dealing with qualities, not quantities, the conditions are not favourable. The same considerations apply to any sphere of human thought and action—Literature, Politics, Industry. As we choose our evidence, so we discover they are beneath contempt or above praise. Modern talk and modern books are full of pseudo-scientific claptrap ; Marxist, Freudian, or pseudo-sociological since the 1920's ; pseudo-physical or pseudo-biological a short time before that. If we attend to these we shall conclude that science is a fraud and the witch of En-dor the mother of all scientists.*

If we are going to make a judgment about the merits of this or that realm of thought and activity, and sooner or later we have to do it, it is almost certainly most satisfactory to look at the best, though with a critical eye, and to ignore the worst. Any normal and healthy activity or institution attracts to itself a lunatic or criminal fringe as soon as it appears successful ; but the fringe is not the significant part. That is not to deny that there are inherently corrupt and evil activities and institutions, and that the worst that can be said of them is significant. If we fasten our attention on the worst aspects of Fascism or Nazism (now mercifully extinct in their original forms), we are not misjudging otherwise beneficent institutions ; we are looking at the Devil and observing that he is black ; even if he is not equally black all over.

Consider for a moment one aspect of pre-scientific thought. The primitive craftsman when he was handling his tools, as he did competently or even better than just competently, was operating ' scientifically ' ; whether he *thought* or not we cannot say, nor could he, but rudiments were there of what later grew to be physical science. If it never entered his head to make this technique the basis for a comprehensive world-view, he was lucky or wise. He was less lucky or wise when the technique at his disposal fell short of fulfilling his desires. Then he was apt to import into what should have been technical thinking ideas derived from other sources, especially from his general world-view, which was in its way religious. As a

* She is, in fact, the step-mother of all technologists. Saul is the father of all politicians who misuse technology.

result he took up superstitions of various sorts, witchcraft and magic ; all of them mixtures of pseudo-technics and pseudo-religion. The primitive fisherman, for instance, constructed his canoe and his fishing gear very well. He knew well enough the right bait to use and the right times and places to fish. So far his technique was good, his methods ' scientific '. Unfortunately all this did not always produce a sufficient supply of fish, or guarantee a safe return from a fishing trip. He therefore resorted to magic to bring the fish and keep off storms. The magic was a set of rules, resembling scientific rules, by which the supernatural powers were supposed to be compelled, bribed, blackmailed or bullied into doing what he required. The drawback to magic is that it is seldom effective (because, as is always explained, more powerful counter-magic is at work). Yet in course of time old sorts of magic are shown up for what they are and abandoned. Better technique is found to be more effective for technical purposes ; so also is better religion for moral purposes, and both are enemies of magic. Improved religion realizes that it is no part of God's function to make good deficiencies in technique or to guarantee success in fishing or other enterprises, however useful. Some people have taken this to imply that God can be left out of account and that any kind of religious world-view is wrong. Few people want genuine religion or genuine science ; most of us prefer some kind of magic.

I cannot avoid contrasting non-scientific thought and scientific in terms of historical progress. There is, however, less difference between primitive and modern thought than many like to suppose who pin their faith to ' progress ', forgetting that there is ' The Rake's Progress ' as well as ' The Pilgrim's Progress ' (cf. John Baillie, *The Belief in Progress*, 1950, Oxford University Press).

A great deal of what follows will sound very old-fashioned to those who follow the latest fashion and assume that whatever is old is wrong. But if the old is always wrong then there is no such thing as science. For newer science has been built on the foundations of older science throughout its history. The necessary assumption has always been and still is that *in the main* the old is right, valid and to be trusted ; though partially, here or there, it may be wrong. Error is discovered because new evidence of things not previously expected comes to light. Thus we can maintain that science provides some valid knowledge at all stages, without assuming that men of science are infallible. We can admit of change of views without committing the ' latest fashion ' fallacy and despising the past.

§3. The Greeks laid the foundations of many sciences, perhaps all except chemistry. Of mathematics and astronomy they produced far more than foundations. By the time the great Alexandrians of the 3rd and 2nd century B.C. had done their work the edifice was built ; on a small scale of course, but neat and tidy and weatherproof. Later work has added more and more rooms.

In the early stages of mathematics and astronomy we can see very well how science proceeds by combining sense experience with reason—perception with conception. Mathematics needs experience for all its vaunted purity and for all its difference from what are clearly observational sciences. These again for all their dependence on sense need reason even at the very beginning. Given an initial scientific impulse ; given more especially the Greek tendency to decide things by argument (the source of all civilized methods of law and government), then mathematics of some sort will develop. As the most abstract of all sciences, needing the minimum of empirical information and of external technical apparatus, there are no hindrances to its development once it begins. By a lucky accident, or error, the Greeks turned from arithmetic in order to study geometry. Starting with an idea that numbers are units, and in some sense spatial, they tried to develop an arithmetical geometry ; that is to say to treat geometry as a *species* of the *genus* arithmetic. At an early stage they came across incommensurables, by finding that some lengths could not be equated with numbers if certain others were so equated. They then decided that there was something fishy about numbers, changed their tactics and treated arithmetic as a *species* of the *genus* geometry. Under the circumstances of the 6th and 5th centuries B.C. this was a

[16]

far more fruitful method, and led to future extensions which
even the genius of Plato could only faintly discern.

That will perhaps suffice to explain the early growth of
mathematics. But why astronomy, among the observational
sciences ? Now the Greeks have often been accused of neglecting observation or of being bad at it, and also of neglecting
experiment which all moderns praise as a specially fruitful
kind of observation. It is of course quite true that the Greeks
expected more from mathematics than there was in mathematics to give ; but so did Descartes, Leibniz and probably
Kant, who had less excuse. On the other hand these modern
critics of ancient Greeks do not seem to know what observation
is ; particularly, how very hard it is to observe anything for
the first time. The critics have never done it for themselves,
they have always relied on observation at second hand,
observations ready made, tested, vouched for and recorded in
books. To experiment for the first time is even more difficult ;
it usually consists of doing something wrong fifty times in
the hope that it may come right the fifty-first time ; it is
always slow, hard, monotonous, unrewarding work. If you
are going to start observing it is well to start with the easiest
kind ; inevitably, that means astronomical observation. The
motions of the stars are already orderly and their order has
been noted by pre-scientific observers for hundreds of years.
In other matters within the realm of physical science there is
very little ready-made order to observe. Order among lifeless
material things, like order in a tidy house, has to be produced
with toil and ingenuity ; with perpetual toil, since things get
disorderly as soon as they are left alone. Why is it that modern
physicists build laboratories at great expense, and install in
them instruments and machines of many kinds at still greater
expense ? The answer is simple—to obtain enough order to
start work, for without the laboratories and instruments, there
is rather more chaos than order about. The Greeks had no
laboratories or apparatus, and perhaps that answer suffices so
far as physics is concerned. In a way it answers both questions
about observation and experiment. But there is also biology,
where order is to be found ready made, though not so very
easily.

§4. I cannot resist pointing out an amusing *faux pas* on this very question committed by a celebrated modern philosopher, who among his other distinctions is a Fellow of the Royal Society. Lord Russell has said that the Greeks were good at devising hypotheses but not much good at observation ; and has cited Aristotle as one of the culprits. In his *Unpopular Essays* (1950, p. 135), he returns to the attack : ' Aristotle could have avoided the mistake of thinking that women have fewer teeth than men by the simple device of asking Mrs. Aristotle to keep her mouth open while he counted. He did not do so because he thought he knew. Thinking you know when in fact you don't is a fatal mistake, to which we are all prone.' It is lucky for Lord Russell that at least he said ' we all ', since he is more prone than Aristotle.

In the first place he has not verified his references ; the one kind of observation that is essential for those who rely on second hand observation, as we all do nowadays. No statement such as Lord Russell attributes to Aristotle appears in *De Partibus Animalium*, which might be taken to consist of assertions for which Aristotle would vouch. The statement which Lord Russell evidently intended to refer to is in the *Historia Animalium* (501 b. 20), where he would have found, ' Males have more teeth than females in man, sheep, goats, swine.' This is in a short paragraph of two sentences, unconnected with what comes before or after. The second sentence of the paragraph, which is less intelligible, appears to contradict what is said elsewhere in the same book. Immediately afterwards comes an account of the irruption of human wisdom teeth which might go word for word into a modern textbook of anatomy. Had Lord Russell looked up the passage he would have altered the wording of what he says ; more important, he would have begun to realize that the *Historia Animalium* is a compilation of *dicta* from various sources, not all equally good and not all vouched for by Aristotle. It is a first attempt at collecting and sorting information for permanent record, the remote ancestor of our textbooks and encyclopædias. It contains everything from reliable first hand reports by competent observers to old wives' tales. In the course of centuries observations have improved and increased and old wives' tales have gradually

dropped out.   Aristotle began it all, though hindered equally
by those who stick to old wives' tales through thick and thin,
and by armchair sceptics.

In the second place, the next paragraph about wisdom
teeth, had he read it, would have made Lord Russell more
cautious.   From what we know of the life of Aristotle, we can
infer that he married in his thirties or later, as indeed was
customary then, certainly after his own wisdom teeth irrupted
(if they did ; some people's never do).   His wife on the other
hand will probably have been in her 'teens on marriage, as was
customary, and almost certainly her wisdom teeth would not
have irrupted.   Aristotle might well have counted his own
teeth and his wife's and found that she had four less than he
had.

§5.   Observation is not such a simple affair as many people
suppose, before they have tried it.   It needs practice, the
familiar is more easily and better observed than the unfamiliar ;
it needs skill, to see the essentials and distinguish them from
unessentials ; above all other things it needs a purpose, some
sort of plan, or at least an aim, and that calls for prior knowledge.   The very first steps of all are the most difficult of
all.   Sometimes they are so difficult that things under people's
very noses wait for centuries before anybody has the wit or
the luck to observe them for the first time (e.g. the fertilisa-
tion of plants and migration of birds).*   The luck never
comes to those without the wit.   What the ordinary man in
the street (or study) is apt to call observation is habit, and
reflects no credit on him if he is right about it.   The credit
belongs to our ancestors who first formed these habits and
then handed them on by example and precept.   Men have
learnt their observation in pursuit of the practical crafts
and techniques of everyday life ; and strictly within those
limits their efforts are pretty good ; outside them not so
good.   The primitive savage, the illiterate peasant, the ordinary
artisan, even the ordinary journalist and university professor
are all accurate and reliable in matters connected with their

* That some birds appear at certain seasons and disappear at others has been
known from time immemorial, but evidence that they *migrate* is relatively recent.

daily work ; all are pretty poor observers outside it. Lord Russell is reliable on matters connected with mathematical logic ; on teeth and on Aristotle he is not.

The methods of observation of the modern man of science are the result of centuries of effort, aided by written, and especially by printed records. The Greeks started from scratch ; to make the observations and write the books, though not, alas, to print them. Both processes are needed ; to make the observation and record it—either by itself is useless. To form part of the scientific account observations must be vouched for by somebody and available to anybody ; they must be public in both these senses. All this means that the apparently simple single observation, if it is to be used, is part only of something very complex, not simple or single. There is no science at all without a society of scientifically interested and competent persons, making, checking and recording ; and their instruments for doing these things.

§6. At the beginning there seems to have been in the Greek world a strong prejudice against the written record ; the Pythagoreans for instance never wrote anything so far as we know. This prejudice was natural among people with well trained verbal memories who knew how easily manuscript records can be garbled by careless or dishonest copyists.* Aristotle and his pupils, and their followers in Alexandria, were responsible for beginning to preserve records, without which there would be no science in the Western world and probably no civilization either.

Experiment is an even more troublesome kind of observation. It is perhaps sufficiently described as controlled observation. Control requires a purpose, a quite definite one, and instruments for control. Sometimes the instruments are found ready to hand ; sometimes not. If they are not ready and have to be invented, then experiment is difficult indeed. At the best it is not easy. The very different history of experiment in physics, chemistry and biology is instructive, for in the first of these difficulties are least, in the third greatest. It is hardly

---

* At best the written word is no more (but no less) than a potted memory available to all who know how to unpot it.

an exaggeration to say that successful biological experiment is almost impossible, but luckily not quite impossible. Full control is never obtained, because living organisms are born and not made. Some degree of control is possible and very often enough for ordinary purposes. Experiment in chemistry might have been (one would suppose) no more difficult than in physics, but chemistry started its career handicapped by greed, fraud and secrecy. So far as the purpose of the experiments of the alchemists was to get something for nothing, the consequences were those to be expected. This is not the whole story and the rest will be told later. (Chapter VII).

Even in physics, experiment as a regular method did not come so easily. I should say that the Greeks did a good deal in the way of experiment, but sporadically, not systematically, and not always recorded. Some experimentation must have preceded Archimedes' foundation of theoretical mechanics (Chapter VI). Some aspects of geometry and astronomy required controlled observations or were aided by models. It is hard to believe that the Five Regular Solids were discovered without constructing models ; if that is not experiment, I do not know what is. It is almost equally hard to believe that any Greek mathematician would have recorded in writing the fact that he or anyone else constructed a model, much less that this record would survive. Yet, by the merest chance we possess parts of a treatise of Archimedes, explaining his use of models to arrive at propositions in solid geometry ; not of course to prove them ; no Greek would have taken a model as providing proof.*

The discovery of the arithmetical ratios underlying the harmonious musical intervals was an experimental discovery, and one of great importance. It was attributed to Pythagoras himself, which puts it back into the legendary early period, but in this case there is no special reason to doubt the attribution. On the other hand the extant accounts of the experiment are by late, unreliable authors who knew little enough of Pythagoras,

---

* Sir Thos. Heath, *The Method of Archimedes*, 1912, p. 13 ; see also the Introduction to the *Quadrature of the Parabola*. Archimedes says he first discovered the theorem by means of mechanics and then exhibited it by means of geometry. Heath, *Archimedes*, 1897, p. 233.

less of science, and could only produce garbled versions.* It is hard to see, though, what Pythagoras could have done but stretch a string tight enough to produce a note when plucked, measure its length, then stop it off at various measured intervals observing at which lengths the note given was the octave (12 : 6), the fifth (12 : 8) and the fourth (8 : 6) ; all together giving the 'Harmonic Proportion', 12 : 8 : 6. As has been well said, this experiment does in principle everything which the experimental method in physics can do. It correlates directly observed regularities with a general formula expressed (by preference) in mathematical terms.

Why did this brilliant experimental discovery lead to no further experiment ? The reply seems to be, how could it be followed up ? A question had been asked and an answer given ; it was complete so far as the ancient world could judge of completeness or the reverse. Many centuries later when the time was ripe for the wave theory of sound, more could be done and was. Even an Archimedes could not see two thousand years ahead ; no more could Pythagoras.

Aristotle quotes an excellent experiment of Empedocles, (Diels, *Vorsokratiker*, Fr. 100) designed to show that air, hitherto supposed to be mere emptiness, is real stuff occupying space like solids and liquids. It marks one of the decisive turning points in physical thought, but both Empedocles and Aristotle are concerned to answer a biological, rather than a physical question ; namely, what is happening when we breathe ? Again, a question had been asked and answered, nothing more seemed to be called for and nothing more was called for till the 16th and 17th centuries, when new problems and new techniques for dealing with them led to the study of the physical properties of gases.

Harvey in the 17th century, an age which was interested in pumps and knew how they worked, carried out a perfectly designed series of experiments to show that the heart works after the manner of a pump. In the 4th century B.C. nobody could have understood them, if they had been shown to him.

* A fragment attributed (doubtfully) to Philolaus of Tarentum (5th century B.C.) mentions the ratios but not the method. Fr. 6 in Diels, *Vorsokratiker*, cf. Freeman, *Ancilla*, p. 74.

The time was not then ripe. (This Principle of Unripe Time is an ambiguous one, but it cannot be dispensed with.)

I should conclude that, given the incentive and opportunity, given a problem and instruments to hand, the Greeks experimented well enough, and showed no greater preference for lazier alternatives than did later men of science. Newton still had cause to complain that many of his contemporaries thought that theory could take the place of experiment.

The genuine historical puzzle of the Western world is why the great men of the 4th and 3rd centuries B.C. had no successors. It may have been that they had done so much that there appeared to be little more to do. In any case, the ' failure ' of the ancient world, if there was a failure, came first in the non-scientific realms of activity, in politics, religion, literature, architecture ; while mathematics, astronomy, physics, and to some extent, medicine, still went ahead. One big difference between the Mediterranean world in which science faded out and the later Western world in which it started again was in technical invention and craftsmanship. As Lewis Mumford has said, the forerunner of modern industry and the machine age is the clock and not the steam engine ; the beginning was in the 13th century or earlier, not the late 18th century (*Technics and Civilization*, 1946, pp. 14-18). The clock was also the forerunner of modern experimental science.

CHAPTER III

ELEMENTS OF GEOMETRY: EUCLID

Euclidean method · The Elements, Book I · Proposition I, 32 · Empirical and non-empirical in Euclid · Post-Euclidean Geometry · Arithmetic and Formal Logic

§1. THE Greeks converted the ancient techniques of calculation and mensuration into the science of mathematics, the first of the physical sciences. It is a science because it is general and uses theory ; instead of trusting to luck, it sees what is implied in technique. Even more, it is science because it possesses methods of proof, entirely new techniques for distinguishing successful practice and valid theory from their opposites. It always includes operations of calculation or mensuration which are performed with objects, even if the objects are only ink on paper, therefore the work of the mathematician is not a completely non-empirical process, if such a process could be supposed to occur. Because it combines proof and theory with action and observation it is, in Kant's terms, reason having insight into what has been constructed according to a plan of its own. Moreover that plan is freely constructed, it is not imposed ; thus mathematics is an art as well as a science.

To consider what the Greek mathematicians did and said it would be best to begin at the beginning ; but the beginnings have perished except for isolated fragments, some reliable hearsay and a good deal of unreliable gossip. However we do possess one complete text, Euclid's *Elements*, which as its name implies, makes a beginning. It goes on to some quite advanced work and includes much that we should now call arithmetic. The difficulty about Euclid is that, like many teachers, he passes quickly over the early stages, taking them to be already familiar or to be picked up as one goes along.

Euclid * begins with the construction of figures and from the figures as constructed his proofs are derived. Construction

---

* In all that follows I am using Sir Thomas Heath's Edition, 3 Vols, 1908. (Cambridge University Press).

is a method of discovery as well as of proof ; you do not know what it is you are going to construct until you have done it. Most of the actual discussion among Greek mathematicians appears to have turned on the solution of Problems of construction, and not the proof of Theorems. On the other hand the proof of a theorem was often the solution of a problem (e.g. *Euclid* I, Props. 47 and 48 solve the problem: To construct a square equal in area to the sum of the areas of any two given squares). Euclid's geometry is, in short, the science of the Drawing Office on which all the sciences of the Workshop depend.

Every schoolboy knows that Euclid knew no algebra, so the poor man had laboriously to construct figures to prove theorems which can now be proved by algebra more easily, more generally and without certain awkward assumptions [e.g. *Euclid* II, Prop. 4 is equivalent to $(a+b)^2 = a^2+2ab+b^2$]. What many schoolboys do not know is that Euclid knew well enough how to dispense with ordinary figures when he wished. Let me therefore begin with a notable example : *Euclid* IX, Prop. 20. This is a theorem with a rather modern flavour about it to the effect that the number of prime numbers is infinite ; or, better, that there can be no greatest prime number, since given any alleged greatest a greater can be constructed. The proof is simple, but it calls for two postulates : (i) the series of natural numbers can be constructed and extended indefinitely by successive addition of units ; (ii) the same series can also be constructed by multiplication, by multiplying the prime numbers (which have no factors but themselves and one) to produce all the composite numbers.

Proof : From the series of natural numbers select the primes in order, i.e. 1, 2, 3, 5, 7, 11, 13, 17, ... Suppose that 17 is the greatest prime number ; multiply it by all the preceding primes then add one to the product. We have now constructed a new number (N) which is not divisible by any of the primes up to and including 17, therefore N is a prime number greater than 17 or a multiple of such a prime. We can repeat the process with the next prime, 19, and with any other given prime number however great.

This is pure arithmetical theory ; it comes into Euclid because he puts arithmetic under the wing of geometry to

[25]

develop what Heath calls the 'geometrical algebra of the Greeks'; namely a general method capable of developing theory and of dealing with difficulties arising out of the discovery of incommensurables. The proposition is also the very purest kind of theory; it is no use. It cannot be applied to problems that arise from the practical uses of calculation. It can only be used to refute without labour or trouble cranks who claim that they have discovered the greatest prime number ($2^{61} + 1$, let us say). Its sole value is that it gives insight into the nature of numbers. Incidentally, when any one can produce a Babylonian text which states and proves this theorem, it will then be time to admit that they possessed a science of arithmetic and not, as would appear, only an advanced technique of calculation, very largely used for propagating astrological superstitions.

I have emphasized the 'purity' of this piece of reasoning and now go on to emphasize that it constitutes a *discovery* about a *subject matter* and is done by means of *constructions*.* Even if you construct by an arbitrary act of will, or invent, or imagine, or call your constructions 'ideal', yet, provided it is done by rule, the construction will have a character of its own and that you will have to discover. Either a series of terms comes to an end or it does not. To discover which you have to 'inspect' the series. The series has been constructed after a plan and the 'inspection' is done by a plan which takes that first plan into account. Inspection means *doing* something, it is *practical*, it uses a *technique*. Until something is done nothing is known. Theory involves contemplation, but till something is done there is nothing to contemplate. Let me add an example where the technique of inspection, so far as I know, has not been found, thus nothing has been done and nothing is known. Prime numbers sometimes, not always, come in pairs, e.g. 17 and 19, 29 and 31. Is there a greatest pair of primes or not?

Euclid begins by setting out operational rules or prescriptions under the headings : Definitions, Postulates, Common Notions. Euclid is careful to avoid the term Axiom

* It is interesting how some writers fight shy of the literal mechanical term 'construct', using instead a biological metaphor, 'generate' a series.

which had already acquired awkward associations, and still has them. He is unfortunate in his term Definition (ὅρος). Some of his definitions are no more than short cuts in terminology ; for instance it is more convenient to say ' semicircle ' than ' figure contained by the diameter of a circle and the circumference cut off by it '. This is a trifle. Most of them are a great deal more ; they are required to explain what is being done when the postulates are used ; they are a necessary part of the operational rules and to be seen along with the relevant postulate in each case. It is important not to take these as dictionary definitions, which had not yet been invented, nor even as the ὅροι for which Socrates sought, which Euclid probably had in mind. Socrates was seeking for a classificatory system of the genus, species and difference type. Euclid needed this, of course, but it was a very simple affair hardly noticed.

Euclid's order of procedure is that of deductive argument ; he arrives at conclusions by showing that they follow of necessity from previously assumed premisses. The order is the logically correct one, but by itself it does not show clearly what is the nature of the subject matter under discussion, nor does it fully display the method used. Neither Euclid nor his predecessors can have first reached all, or perhaps any, of the conclusions by the process of argument or in the order set out. The order is an order of ' calculation ' not of thought. There must have been an empirical or partly empirical process of discovery which came first and which neither Euclid nor any one else says anything about. This reticence is natural enough in Euclid, though tantalizing. It is far more tantalizing and less natural in some of his successors. For instance Aristarchus deals with the *Sizes and Distances of the Sun and Moon,* and Archimedes with the *Equilibrium of Floating Bodies,* as though they had arrived at everything *a priori.* Newton's exposition in his *Principia* is still in part on the ancient model. Wallis (quoted by Heath, *History of Greek Mathematics,* Vol. II, p. 21) said ' not only Archimedes but nearly all the ancients so hid from posterity their method of Analysis (though it is clear they had one) that more modern mathematicians found it easier to invent a new analysis than to seek out the old '.

It is perhaps worth remembering that Euclidean terminology which now sounds so very technical, consisted in his day
mainly of words from common speech, given a specialized
meaning for his special purposes. Thus ' isosceles triangle ',
which now needs to be explained from the beginning to the
enquiring schoolboy was to Euclid's contemporaries roughly
' three kneed thing with equal legs ' ; a bit metaphorical
perhaps but calling for little explicit comment. This had the
advantage that it left no doubt that geometry dealt with objects
or things, idealized perhaps, taken as representative and not
' in the raw ', and perhaps even limiting cases of thingness.

There were disadvantages too. Euclid is not as explicit
or complete in his statements as we should like. He took over
a great deal from common technical folk-lore just as he took
over some of the tools of the carpenter and stone-mason and
surveyor ; straight edge, dividers and compasses. The
carpenter tests the straightness of his edge by putting one end
to one eye, raising the other to the light and squinting along it,
according to Euclid's definition (apparently) and making use
of the straightness of light rays in a homogeneous medium.
The carpenter also uses the alternative test of the stretched
string ; the shortest distance between two points. As for the
rigidity of bodies ; Euclid rejects the obviously non-rigid and
is content with that.

Folk-lore is not always very precise and is often at a loss when
taken beyond its ordinary range of operation. The modern
method of formalization evades difficulties but does not always
overcome them. You can set up arbitrary but explicit symbolic systems asserting identities and non-identities between
various symbolic groups and develop these by working through
the permitted regroupings and combinations and you can leave
it at that. You also leave it an impenetrable mystery how this
' pure ' system is to be ' applied ' to the physical world. The
mystery can be evaded by saying again that explicit but equally
arbitrary identifications are to be made. The puzzles are
thus referred back to the ' applied ' mathematician who uses
' common sense ', like Euclid. Euclid goes a little way in the
direction of formalization, by putting his basic propositions
first (most of them) and beginning the list with definitions, as

[28]

though they could stand by themselves. In the list of definitions the most abstract and ambiguous come at the beginning, and the more concrete later. Thus you can point to a triangle or a circle, a visible area with a visible boundary, even if coarser and more irregular than it should be. Whatever visible object you point to, it will not be a point (excuse the pun).

§2. I propose to reverse this process in part and hope the reasons for it will appear as we go along. Let us start then with bodies, with actual physical objects which can be moved, split, sliced, chipped, rubbed, carved and otherwise handled in the workshop. Then from them by a process of abstraction go on to those special, idealized bodies that are handled on the drawing board and then to the imaginative relations that theory contemplates. The primary assumptions that Euclid requires are that there are bodies with determinate mechanical properties and relations, which are stable and recognizable by sight and touch combined, e.g. that ABC is a triangle, the side AB longer than BC, and that K is a circle.* He also assumes that these specimens can be taken as representative. These

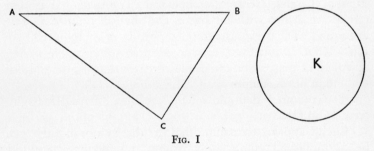

Fig. I

assumptions belong to arithmetic and logic, as well as to geometry. Geometry needs special assumptions of its own in addition. Those that Euclid makes explicit in the First Book are set out below, in the order given by Heath, but expanded and annotated, and with the Definitions put in with the Postulates and Common Notions where called for.

* The figure is drawn and seen at the same time. Blind people could engrave and feel, not quite so quickly and easily, but well enough. I shall use visual terminology for convenience, but it should be read as translatable into haptic terms.

POSTULATES

1. Between any two points on a plane surface one straight line and one only can be drawn.

The required definitions are Nos. 1-7, defining Points, Lines, points as limits of Lines, Straight Lines, Surfaces, Lines as limits of surfaces, Plane Surfaces.

These all taken together imply postulates about (i) Rigid Bodies, (ii) Straight Edges for drawing lines, (iii) Plane Surfaces. The gist of them is that with straight edges we can draw straight lines on plane surfaces and that straight edges and plane surfaces are in contact at all points. (Consider also how Poincaré defines a straight line as an axis of rotation.)

2. Any straight line can be produced indefinitely in either direction.

This implies the postulates (i), (ii), (iii) above and also a corollary that plane surfaces as well as lines can be extended indefinitely in all directions.

3. With any point on a plane surface as centre a circle of any diameter can be drawn.

The required definitions are Nos. 13-17, of Boundaries, Figures, Circles, Centres, Diameters. The gist of it is that circles are drawn with compasses and that all radii of a circle are equal. The previously implied postulates are required here too.

4. All right angles are equal, and greater than acute and less than obtuse angles.

The required definitions are Nos. 8-12, of Angles, Right, Acute and Obtuse.

Euclid appears to assume that the three kinds of angle can be distinguished immediately by eye, but no new postulate seems to be called for. He has the apparatus for proving which are which, given that, when two straight lines intersect, all four angles are right or else none are.

5. The postulate of parallels—to be discussed later.

Euclid appears to require some more postulates, but those which give the trouble are mentioned here. They are (1), (2), (3), (5), the postulate of Parallels, and No. 4 of the Common Notions, to be discussed.

COMMON NOTIONS

1. If A = B and B = C, then A = C.
2. If A = B and C = D, then A+C = B+D.
3. If A = B and C = D, then A−C = B−D.

These call for definitions of equality, addition and subtraction.

4. Magnitudes that coincide are equal.

This is strictly a geometrical postulate. It means that there are rigid bodies and that equality can be determined by super-position ; in other words we can use dividers.

5. The whole is greater than the part.

Apart from (4) these are rules of arithmetic. A commutative rule for addition and subtraction is also called for. As Euclid allows you to count the sides of a figure, he really requires arithmetic too, and therefore the special rules needed to construct the number series.

All these rules, explicit and implicit, taken together provide specifications or prescriptions for measurements of lengths, angles and areas, and also, when we come to solid geometry, volumes. In the same way Ohm's Law provides a prescription for measuring electrical resistance, and indirectly therefore for measuring current and potential. I mention this, not only to keep Workshop science in touch with Drawing Office science, but because both sets of prescriptions require ' ideal conditions ' to be precise.

These rules are not stated as fully, explicitly or generally as possible, but since they are meant to be shown in use, that need not be a fatal defect. To attempt to state such rules in words, *in vacuo* and completely, leads to formulæ that look tautologous or silly. The tactual and visual process of drawing the figure and seeing what it is is not a luxury but a necessity : it is needed for intuition. Intuitions are concrete events, they arise in particular situations. They are not precise but approximate. (More precision can be obtained by formalization but not always without distortion.) Yet they are the process of seeing the universal in the particular.

Our basic judgments arising out of these intuitions are of spatial exclusion, inclusion, coincidence and non-coincidence.

Thus we can see that A is inside the figure not outside, B outside not inside and that A and B are different.

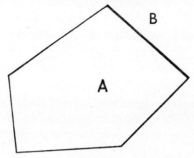

Fɪɢ. II

For Euclid the most important judgments are those which arise out of coincidence, equivalence and plenitude of areas ; for instance that the area of every rectilinear polygon can be divided exactly without remainder into a sum of triangular areas ; and so also can the area of every triangle be divided into the sum of the areas of two right-angled triangles, thus :

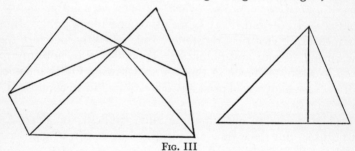

Fɪɢ. III

Try to put such judgments into words alone and they sound tautologous ; consider the figures and they are seen to be far from tautologous. Remember the famous erroneous proof that all triangles are isosceles. It depends upon constructing something inaccurately and failing to notice the discrepancies. (Cf. W. E. Johnson, *Logic*, Vol. II, pp. 206 *seq.*)

All this applies to arguments based directly on the constructed figure. There are also arguments for which no construction can actually be drawn, and arguments with substitute symbols such as modern arithmetic uses. Notice

that (*a*) 2+2 = 4, is a shorthand substitute for (*b*) (1+1)+
(1+1) = 1+1+1+1. In (*a*) sensory spatial intuition has
been pushed into the background ; in (*b*) it remains in the
foreground, and we can *see* that a dyad and another dyad make
up a tetrad. Once the values of the substitutes in terms of the
representative symbols have been learnt off by heart, the
original intuition can be forgotten. Indeed it seems trivial and
the substitutes are more convenient. This convenience is
important, because new operations can be done with the
substitutes and not without them.

The notion of equality * as applied to plane figures is left
vague by Euclid. He appears to require three notions : (1)
congruence, (2) equivalence of areas, without similarity of
figure, (3) similarity of figure, without equivalence of areas.
Congruent figures (1) have the maximum identity or sameness
possible, those that are equivalent (2) only a specific kind.
Similarity (3) is a difficult notion. It is assumed that all circles
are similar, also all squares, all equilateral triangles, all isosceles
right-angled triangles, and so on. How do we know it ? The
discussion of this will have to come later.

For Euclidean geometry in general (2) is the important
notion. It can be shown that any parallelogram is bisected by
its diagonal to give two congruent triangles, and also that it
can be bisected by a straight line drawn parallel to the sides to
give two congruent parallelograms. Thus the parallelogram

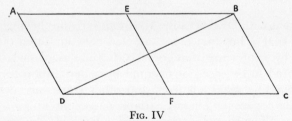

FIG. IV

ABCD is bisected by the diagonal BD and also by EF. Clearly
the triangle which is a half of the whole figure and the parallelogram which is a half are not congruent. They are in fact as
dissimilar as rectilinear figures can be, yet in some way equal,

* Equality (ἰσότης) was originally a legal, economic and social notion.
Later it was applied to mathematics and physics. The same is true of law (νόμος)
and cause (αἴτιος).

namely as to their areas. This is a most significant discovery, partly sensory intuition, partly not. Granted also that any rectilinear figure can be reduced to a rectangle of equivalent area and that the area of a rectangle is given by the product of the lengths of its sides, there is the key to ancient geometrical algebra, which was itself the key to the dynamical algebra of the moderns on which physical theory is based. The theory of equivalent areas, that we find in *Euclid*, raised the problem which so greatly intrigued the Greeks : to find a rectilinear figure equivalent in area to a given circle.

Congruence is subject to an empirical test. Euclid's method of superposition, used once in I, Prop. 4, and once only, is an appeal to common experience of the behaviour of rigid bodies. You can say if you like that equality has to be defined in terms of superposability, and superposability in terms of equality, so that it is tautological to say the triangle ABC is

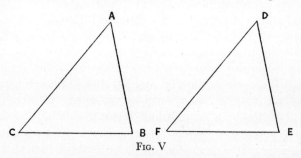

Fig. V

congruent with DEF because AB equals DE and the angle BAC equals EDF. But that is because you have forgotten that you learnt by experience that some bodies are rigid and can be discovered to be equal or unequal by superposition (or other corresponding manipulation), and other bodies are not rigid and only possess temporary, variable or ' apparent ' not ' real ' equality. The triangles are assumed to be rigid or in some way equivalent to rigid bodies ; sensory spatial intuitions applied to the figures tell us they are equal and the hackneyed nature of the whole business then leads to talk about tautologies. If it so happened that all the red things we came across were also hot, and all the hot things also red, sooner or later somebody would come along and say that because of this equivalence

' hot ' and ' red ' had the same meaning and that it was tautologous to say of anything red that it was hot.

Equivalence of areas without congruence is not subject to direct sensory intuition and requires roundabout empirical tests, so that judgments of equivalence are much more like paradoxes than tautologies. Such judgments require discursive reasoning. If there are such things as *a priori* synthetic propositions, then these are they.

If this interpretation of the postulates and axioms be accepted it will appear that Euclidean geometry deals with those things, those only, which occupy limited volumes of space, so that if they are in this place they are not in that, and which also have the properties of recognizable, stable, rigid bodies. In more general terms, its realm of discourse presupposes the Law of Excluded Middle. Whatever might conceivably be said about the other so-called Laws of Thought, this one has to be a law of things, of the observed behaviour of certain constituents of the physical world. If there are other things whose observed behaviour is different then they will be excluded from the Euclidean realm, by an interesting extension of the Law of Excluded Middle ; but no other untoward consequence will follow. Further, Euclidean geometry is concerned with the realm of discourse where Descartes' rules of method apply strictly ; where we can by direct inspection arrive at clear and distinct ideas ; where we can break up a complex subject matter into simple elements ; where we can deal with these one by one in order, until by so doing we have completed our survey of the whole and left nothing out of account. It now remains to see how this interpretation works out.

§3. Let us consider a familiar but important and difficult theorem ; namely *Euclid* I, Prop. 32. It is required to prove that the sum of the angles of any triangle equals two right angles. Like so many of the important theorems it deals with the summation of quantities. Apart from *Euclid* I, 13, required for it, it is the first where quantities are found to be equivalent in spite of being composed of different constituents, i.e. two right angles are two and are not identical with any set of three angles. One could deal with the theorem in a direct empirical sort of way by superposition. Rotate the base line BC of the triangle ABC (see Fig. VI below) round the angle at B till it coincides with AB, then in the same sense round the angle at A till it coincides with AC, then round the angle at C till it returns to the original position ; it will then have rotated exactly half a circle. It is pretty clear that Euclid would have condemned this as an underhand trick if put forward as a proof. But why ? Is not the whole notion of summation (the basis of arithmetic) the notion of a physical process of super-, juxta-, im-, or com-position ? Then we formalize or symbolize it and it becomes one symbol taking the place of several.

Let us consider Euclid's procedure. He says : ' Let ABC be a triangle.'

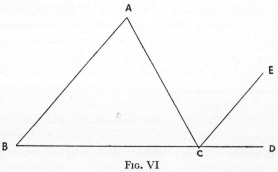

Fɪɢ. VI

That means any triangle (whatever ' any ' may mean). It also means (more intelligibly) that he provides or we provide an actual specimen of the kind of thing he is going to argue about. He continues : ' Produce the side BC and through the point C draw CE parallel to the side AB.' All this requires the combination of action, sensory intuition and reasoning already mentioned. The purpose of the construction is to connect the question to be answered with what he has already proved about the properties of parallels and straight lines intersecting them, and with his demonstration of how to draw a line parallel to another. To quote Kant, you do not prove theorems about triangles either by looking at triangles, as Hume could be accused of assuming, or by analyzing the concept of a triangle, as Leibniz could be accused of assuming ; but by imposing on the subject matter something that 'reason has constructed after a plan of its own' so as to have 'insight'.

There is no need to give the rest of the proof, but one point remains to be noticed. What Euclid does explicitly is to show that in this one solitary, particular triangle ABC the sum of its three angles equals two right angles. He requires a further step, always stated explicitly ; namely, that what is true of ABC is true of all triangles or any triangle. W. E. Johnson (*Logic*, Vol. II, pp. 189 *seq.*) calls this process *Intuitive Induction.* Induction it certainly is, as it proceeds from particular to general ; yet it is not 'problematic' like the generalization 'cattle chew the cud'. It raises the interesting question : why is it that, having seen one specimen of a triangle and finding that its three angles equal two right angles, we at once decide that this is also true of all the countless triangles we have not seen ; whereas we are so much more cautious about cows. We should not dream of generalizing from observation of one cow and even after seeing many chewing the cud we still only say that it is highly probable that all cows chew the cud (though we should be worried if we found one that did not, and possibly the cow would be worried too). Of course there are ways out of the difficulty by means of the distinction between 'all' and 'any' ; by talk about 'ideal' entities, and so on. Most people are content to say that the triangle ABC is taken symbolically, as representing its kind.

As is well known, Euclid was in some difficulty over this Prop. 32. Aristotle mentions that the proofs of his day were circular. Euclid's is not, at least *prima facie*, but it depends upon the notorious *Postulate of Parallels*, which I have not yet dealt with. The Postulate is used once only to prove Prop. 29, which is needed for Prop. 32. Prop. 32 can be confirmed by measurement and could be treated as an empirical generalization ; it could be treated as self-evident ; it could stand as a postulate. The postulate of parallels cannot be confirmed by measurement ; it is not particularly self-evident. For more than two thousand years mathematicians tried in vain to prove it. In short there is something queer about it. The original form is : 'If a straight line falling on two straight lines makes the interior angles on the same side less than two right angles, the two straight lines if produced indefinitely meet on that side on which the angles are less than two right angles.' It can be seen by sensory spatial intuition that, on that side on which the lines diverge the angles are greater and on that side on which

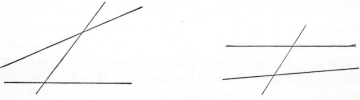

Fig. VII

they converge the angles are less, and the greater the divergence the greater the angles, the greater the convergence the less the angles. Further than that sensory spatial intuition does not go, and no line can in fact be produced indefinitely. More modern formulations do not seem any better. ' Playfair's ' Axiom is : ' Two intersecting straight lines cannot both be parallel to a third straight line.' It has the advantage of generality and might well stand as the negative corollary of which *Euclid* I, Prop. 30 is the positive, but it can hardly stand by itself. Its negative form also suggests comparison with the physical Postulates of Impotence (see p. 123).

The difficulty, if it can be separated from the primary difficulties about the uniqueness of straight lines and right angles, is that only quite small figures can be drawn with ease and their properties intuited by sight. Euclid's geometry so far as it depends upon construction of a figure and intuitive induction is the geometry of things not too small to be seen and not too large to be seen all at once ; man-sized and man-made. The whole set of notions : straight lines, indefinite production of straight lines, parallels, the postulate of parallels, all depend on the assumption that large figures, however large, are similar to small ones however small. We now know that as a pro- position about physical objects this is totally false and as a proposition about abstract space necessarily suspect. (See Appendix.)

We could, if we cared to take the trouble, draw very long lines on the earth's surface (we have nowhere else to draw

[38]

them). We should have to define straightness in terms of the shortest distance between points. We should then find that straight lines could not be produced indefinitely for they would form closed figures, namely Great Circles round the earth. We should also find that we could not draw two distinct Great Circles without their intersecting in two points. We could draw equidistant and non-intersecting lines, e.g. Parallels of Latitude, but they would not be straight, would not be the shortest distance between points, except for the Equator, which is a Great Circle. If we started measuring up the magnitudes of the angles of triangles we should find that *Euclid* I, Prop. 32 did not hold ; for example any two meridians of longitude cut the equator at right angles and yet meet at the North Pole to form a triangle, and the angle at the Pole may be anything up to two right angles. It is all very disappointing.

Of course you may say these are not plane figures ; they are drawn on a curved surface. Perhaps they are, but they are drawn on the only surface available. Any other figures must be 'ideal' figures, belonging, not to any actual space, but to a 'heaven' of Platonic Forms, invisible and intangible.*

I have put the matter in this way, because Platonic Forms are unfashionable ; at least they are never mentioned in polite society. Let me try to put it more moderately. There is an empirical side to the Euclidean argument, in constructing figures and in the sensory intuitions that go with the process. That empirical side enters with the definition of a straight line and the First Postulate. There is also a non-empirical side which comes in with the Second Postulate, which means, among other things, that a straight line can be produced indefinitely. Straight lines never are ; all actual lines are finite and most are pretty short. The non-empirical side comes in more clearly still with the notion of parallels. Straight lines which are ten inches long, ten yards or ten miles, may not intersect and yet may not be parallel.

We can see this in the first propositions about parallels, *Euclid* I, Prop. 27-31, which are essential to the whole theory

---

* We have no access to any part of space except by means of mechanical-optical instruments, i.e. by using the properties of radiant energy and rigid bodies. The concept of empty space is a theoretical construction, as empty by itself as the space.

of non-congruent figures of equivalent areas. The last of these is a problem ; to draw a straight line through a given point parallel to a given straight line. It presupposes Prop. 27, which is a proposition about parallel straight lines. The procedure is not so odd as it sounds, as the proof of Prop. 27 does not depend upon anybody's ability to draw parallel straight lines. That is because, like many of Euclid's important proofs, it is by *reductio ad absurdum*. The figure drawn is a caricature or a figure of non-parallel straight lines. *Direct* sensory intuition is not called upon.

The proposition to be proved is that, if a straight line falling on two other straight lines, makes the alternate angles equal, then the two straight lines will be parallel. As De Morgan pointed out it is the negative equivalent of Prop. 16, which is required for the proof. Prop. 16 says that if one side of a triangle be produced the exterior angle is greater than either of the interior opposite angles. The proof of Prop. 27 is as follows :—

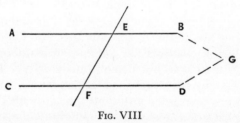

FIG. VIII

If AB and CD are not parallel then they will meet on being produced ; suppose that they meet at G on the side of B and D. Then EFG is a triangle and (from *Euclid* I, Prop. 16) the exterior angle AEF is greater than the interior opposite angle EFG. But this is contrary to the hypothesis, therefore the two lines do not meet on the side of B and D. Similarly they can be shown not to meet on the side of A and C ; therefore they must be parallel.

Here direct sensory spatial intuition is not enough and the symbolism is not quite as previously described. Instead of a specimen being produced to argue about by pointing to it at each stage, it is admitted that no actual specimen can be shown, and what is shown is something different. The argument

[40]

therefore proceeds beyond the scope of specimens and intuitions, introducing a non-sensory element. You can *see* that something *is* so ; you cannot *see* directly that something else is impossible or absurd, because it is not there to see. But you can try to make something and find it a failure, as Euclid does here.

§4. A peculiarity of Euclidean method remains to be noticed, namely that it does not call for evidence or testimony in the way that ordinary observational and inductive sciences do. We can, in principle, begin at the beginning, an absolute beginning, and work through to an end, within limits an absolute end and completion of the argument. We can do it all ourselves, for ourselves ; we do not need the testimony of others (again, in principle). We cannot entirely avoid relying on memory, but can do with a minimum of that as long as we have a written record to refer to. In this kind of way alone can we survive the Cartesian method of doubt and operate always with clear and distinct ideas. As Spinoza says, the beginner who has worked carefully and thoroughly through the argument leading to *Euclid* I, Prop. 32 knows as much about *that* subject as the most experienced and accomplished mathematician. Later knowledge enlarges ; it does not, given sufficient care in the early stages, alter or destroy anything.* Lastly, we can approach nearly to a science of the present and not of the past. Because each can work through from beginning to end for himself, and in simple cases do it ' in his head ' with ' private incommunicable symbols '.† The method is in a sense the most ' subjective ', but the extent of agreement that obtains makes it also the most ' objective '. The extent of agreement must not be exaggerated ; it is only agreement *in the long run* and *of those qualified to give an opinion.*

Observational sciences are first of all records of past events, and to that extent historical ; they depend upon memory and the co-operation of a number of different observers. Robinson Crusoe on his desert island could have gone a long way in

---

* This may in certain favoured instances be true of empirical generalizations —*mutatis mutandis.* But a great deal of *mutandis* is called for.

† Strictly self-contradictory phrases—perhaps they may be pardoned.

mathematics ; given the native ability there was hardly anything he could not have discovered for himself ; but in the
other sciences he would have been hopelessly handicapped.
He could make an inventory of things on the island and keep a
chronicle of events, but these would not be even the beginnings
of the factual sciences or of history ; only materials for what we
actually possess, a novel.

I have been maintaining that Euclidean geometry contains
both an empirical and a non-empirical element. The traditional view was that axioms or other basic propositions had to
be self-evident and if self-evident were *a priori*. My contention
is that what easily impresses itself as self-evident is likely to be
of the nature of a wide, common, and thus unnoticed, generalization from experience. It may well be no more than a good
approximation or useful simplification that applies over a wide
and familiar range, but not true universally nor precisely.

At the present day more trouble is liable to be caused by
asserting that there is a non-empirical element other than the
purely formal. It is generally held that the only legitimate
kind of *a priori* consists of formal rules such as the principles
of logic are supposed to be. I have made the heretical suggestion
that there may be material *a priori* elements in Euclid's
geometry, metaphysical jumps, the work of the creative
imagination.* When they were first made they probably
appeared as paradoxes ; later they passed unnoticed or were
taken to be conventions, truths by definition or tautologies.
On this I need say no more here than that conventions survive
in use because they are found to be convenient, otherwise they
fall out of use ; that a skilled verbalist can always make
definitions look purely verbal and by similar means make
assertions look tautologous, unless actually self-contradictory.
What underlies the talk about conventions, definitions and
tautologies is the fact that the *a priori* element is inserted by
means of a choice between alternatives ; it follows an *arbitrium*
and in that sense is arbitrary. Once the choice is made and
turns out a success it acquires a look of perfect innocence ;
common sense finds that it is just common sense, and each

* These are more easily seen in the sciences which are explicitly observational ;
cf. C. IV, §2 and C. VI, §2.

philosopher finds that it is just whatever it ought to be, according to his own theory.

In a word, I am trying to show that Euclidean geometry is part of physics, the very first part which paved the way for all the rest. It is still mathematics, though not pure mathematics, if there is such a thing. It is also in part metaphysics, as are all sciences.

§5. Granted that there are modern branches of 'pure' mathematics which can properly be called geometries, no Euclidean proposition can be derived from them without first introducing the empirical presuppositions or hypotheses of Euclid, and without at least one process of sensory intuition to establish the Euclidean interpretation of what was originally a pure, that is to say ambiguous notation, without significance in terms of physical space. The pure mathematician may talk about 'space', but it is a courtesy title to which his entities (whatever they may be) have no legal claim. An elementary illustration will explain this and perhaps put the Euclidean position more clearly.

Euclid II, Prop. 4 proves by geometrical algebra the relation now usually written as $(a+b)^2 = a^2 + 2ab + b^2$ where a and b are straight lines and a^2 and b^2 the squares with sides a and b respectively, and ab the rectangle with sides a and b. The Euclidean method is clumsy and restricted in scope. It cannot be applied to numerical relations without rather curious assumptions. The modern algebraical method is neat, easy and completely general. Its generality is that of ambiguity ; a and b may be anything, or, rather, what they may be nobody knows and nobody cares. The operation of addition may be almost anything, provided it is not some other operation. Euclid on the other hand is precise and unambiguous, his magnitudes are carefully specified, they are angles, lengths, areas and volumes, and nothing else. His process of addition is a physical process. Each process of adding a length to a length, an angle to an angle, an area to an area is specific and different, each must be done in its own proper way and that way can be precisely defined. The specifications are not given verbally, because the method of drawing the figure and our

D   [43]

sensory intuitions of it do what is needed and look after the precision of the process. The whole business is physical and as long as it is taken no further there is no difficulty.

Difficulties come in when geometrical magnitudes such as lengths and areas are taken as equivalent to numbers. If a length is equivalent to a number, then the sum of two numbers should be a length. How can the product of two numbers, which is only a sum of sums be supposed equivalent to an area, as for Euclid ? Surely there is some jiggery-pokery about the process ? Indeed there is (or was). It began with the Pythagorean method of representing numbers as patterns of dots or pebbles. A line would be taken as a row, and then obviously . . and . . . equals . . . . . ; but any number that has factors can be represented as an oblong (e.g. : : : equals . . multiplied by . . .). This was the physicalizing of numbers, taking them as things with magnitude. It led to serious trouble over the question of incommensurables, but had its uses. Provided we leave numbers undefined and ambiguous, and accept as a brute fact, left unexplained, that not all numbers are commensurable, then we can use the method of geometrizing arithmetic successfully. This success was the first great triumph of the Principle of Increasing Ambiguity, which has guided mathematicians ever since.

A further triumph of the principle is arithmeticizing geometry, begun by Descartes. If we leave the notions of number and of addition ambiguous we can make numbers stand for anything we like. Descartes made a pair of numbers stand for a point and sets of pairs for a line in plane geometry, and so the trick was done ; a less disreputable trick than the first, and one that made the solution of many problems so quick and easy that the ancient mathematicians must turn in their graves with envy. Now, in rectilinear Cartesian co-ordinates the equation $ax+by+c = 0$ stands for a Euclidean straight line, but in that system of co-ordinates only. By constructing an appropriate co-ordinate system, we can make the equation stand for a spiral, or indeed almost any kind of open curve. I have said 'constructing' a system of co-ordinates, not 'defining', to indicate that the initiating of a system of co-ordinate geometry calls for postulates and a sensory intuition.

[44]

The Cartesian system requires the Euclidean assumptions about straight lines, right angles, and parallels. However, it calls for one sensory intuition only, at the beginning, and perhaps one more at the end, instead of a whole lot of them throughout the argument.

The use of the Principle of Increasing Ambiguity makes it less and less necessary, in defining terms, to say what anything is though it is still necessary to say what it is not. Clearly there is a limit beyond which such a process cannot be pushed. In other words, the Principle of Increasing Ambiguity is subject to a Law of Diminishing Returns. In this it is like Occam's Razor—it may be considered a form of the Razor. At any rate both are labour saving devices ; and scarcity of labour is what makes labour worth saving. As soon as we have saved enough to have a surplus we need save no more.

§6. I have been arguing on the assumption that Euclidean geometry is in the first place a way of handling things ; that because of that it is a way of seeing things ; and that it is not a way of talking about things, except incidentally. You can talk about geometry, as I have been talking or rather writing, but that is not *doing* geometry. Geometry is not a kind of language, though language can be used about it. The use of substitute symbols (algebraic equations) in place of representative symbols (actual drawn figures) does not fundamentally alter what is done, but does call for an imaginative jump and new operational rules or conventions for using the new symbols.

This assumption need not stop short of modern symbolic logic, or as I prefer to call it Basic Arithmetic (Cf. *Philosophical Quarterly* 1955, Vol. 5, p. 267). No amount of formalization gets rid of facts, or the handling of things.* It confines the handling to very sophisticated things ; ink marks on paper and the like, including to a small extent spoken sounds. These new things are still tools, artifacts made for a purpose, like the old Euclidean straight edge and dividers. To fulfil their purpose they are made and handled according to rules. The

---

* Formalizing is a way of abstracting and generalizing that is useful up to a point. Beyond that point it becomes formal*ism*, the kind of metaphysics that reduces everything to nothing.

rules are not part of the handling but have to be communicable from one person to another ; they are linguistic. That is why in the paper referred to I compared mathematics and logic with games. To play the game of golf you have to play according to the rules, but it is the game you play not the rules. To instruct a beginner in the game and the use of the rules language is needed throughout. Once the game has been learned and provided nobody breaks any rules, language is quite superfluous during the game. It is needed before the game begins for two players to arrange where, when and how to play ; it is needed again, when they have both holed out on the 18th green, to agree who has won and by how much. There are people who suppose that golf can be played by talking ; ' bore ' is the politest epithet possible to apply to them. One of the difficulties confronting modern logic is that too many ' bores ' have talked about it and few have actually played it.

I must now ask leave to be a bore for a little longer, on the pretext of instructing a beginner. In order to play the game of Basic Arithmetic (Aristotelian Logic is a not-so-basic form of it) we need to make a special set of symbols as our tools. First of all we need symbols for ' something ' or ' anything ', and also a symbol for ' nothing '. The first may be I or A or B. The second will be O. Our first postulate is that we make this distinction between something and nothing, or what exists and what does not exist, or what is in play and out of play. A symbol for ' nothing ' causes difficulties, because the symbol is something and only pretends to be nothing (as in the story of Odysseus and the Cyclops). This is the first of the paradoxes that have to be faced and swallowed. The absence of a symbol causes still greater difficulties, so one symbol for ' nothing ' we must have and one only. No number or variety of nothings amounts to anything (except, of course, when we decide for very special reasons that it is only a very little one).

For one kind of basic arithmetic no terms or calculi are needed except I, and O ; that is for the construction of what have been called Truth Tables. They are useful constructions, perhaps the most useful that modern logic has devised, but no useful purpose is served by dragging in Truth and Falsehood

at this stage, or at any stage. ' Yes ' and ' No ' or ' In ' and
' Out ' will do. To construct such tables we need a set of
postulates for the various operations we propose to perform
on our calculi or with them. I shall not go into them here
except for the first and most troublesome, in which we are
already implicated with our distinction between I and O.
That is to say we have to take some things as being the same or
equal and others as being different or unequal. Once we
grant that our somethings are plural and spatially and tempor-
ally distributed, then some are reckoned as being the same
or equal, others being different or unequal. We write : A,A,A,
and then B,B,B ; and we agree to take all the A's as the same
or equal (though obviously they are not) and similarly all the
B's. We agree to take any A as different from any B, except
when in special cases and for special reasons we take them to
be the same. (When it comes to ingenious fiction Odysseus is
hopelessly outclassed by the logicians.) Thus we need operative symbols so that we can make $A = A$, $B = B$ always,
$A \neq B$ generally but sometimes $A = B$; also $A \neq O$, $B \neq O$,
except, of course, when we deliberately make $A = O$ or
$B = O$. We need not go into operations ' and ' or ' or ', for
we have enough on our hands, since clearly Compatibility and
Incompatibility have been brought in as well as Identity
and Non-identity.

Having equipped ourselves with symbolic calculi and
symbolic operations to perform on them we find that however
arbitrary and conventional our rules were initially, in the
sense that some of them could have been made different, yet
once the rules are made there are certain things we cannot do
and certain things we can. This is the much publicised
' logical necessity '. I submit that it is also physical or
geometrical necessity. Whatever we say about our operations,
they are still operations on things which have spatial and
temporal relations like all other things. We make marks on
paper and do with them only such things as can be done with
marks on paper. Formalization does not abolish this
geometrical necessity ; it emphasizes it. (Perhaps the Greeks
were right to take geometry, the science of spatial order, as
fundamental.) Moreover, everything that is done on paper,

because of this geometrical necessity, has some applicability to the physical world, it is already part of it. There is no absolutely pure logic or mathematics.

It is possible to take words and phrases, parts of speech, especially subjects and predicates, and use them like calculi, as if units and atomic. That is what Aristotelian Logic did, but it also invented its own type of calculi, for constructing the forms of propositions : e.g. ' S a P ' stands for any universal affirmative. The classical logicians then set up their test constructions, the Square of Opposition, and the Moods and Figures of the Syllogism. These have done useful work and nothing can be said against them except that the work is limited and the limits clearly seen. I suspect that the work which the modern symbolic systems do is also limited and the limits already in sight.

Having used subjects and predicates successfully as calculi it is tempting to suppose that you can go further and use not only parts of speech but whole units of speech (if there are such things) in the same way. Aristotelian logic already went some distance in this direction. I do not say that this breaks any absolutely rigid rules, if there are such rules. But I suspect that it is Gamesmanship according to Mr. Stephen Potter's definition (How to Win at Games without Actually Cheating). The first reason for this suspicion is that it brings in Truth and Falsehood and if there is anything in all that the formalizers have said, that is precisely what nobody should ever do in formal logic. The second is that no complete linguistic process, even if you call it one proposition or one sentence, is atomic or even unitary. Any supposed unit is snatched arbitrarily out of a process of communication between persons within a context. It cannot be shifted without change from person to person or context to context. Subjects or predicates, as parts of speech, can function as units and even as atoms, because they are no more than parts. The third reason is that it causes confusion between playing the game and talking about it.

The Aristotelian logicians enunciated three fundamental principles, which they called The Laws of Thought; of Identity, Contradiction and Excluded Middle. The last I have mentioned above ; and there seems to be no difficulty about it if

it is taken, not as belonging to thought specially, but as
belonging to physics or geometry. It may well be expressed in
the form : you cannot put one thing in two places at one time,
nor two things in one place at one time. Thus you have to
decide what you are going to put uniquely where, or you do
not put anything anywhere. The Law of Contradiction is
better taken in terms of compatibility and incompatibility.
Again it is a law of physics and of operations. You can do
many things together so long as they are compatible, but
certain things you cannot do together at one time and place
because they are incompatible. You have to discover which
kind of operations are which, because they depend on the
physical properties of bodies, including human bodies. If
you decide to walk, you cannot then and there swim or fly.
If you decide to turn left you cannot then and there turn right
or go straight on. If there were a world of pure thought or
pure visual perception or pure language, as many philosophers
appear to suppose, anything would be compatible with
anything.

So far so good ; the Law of Identity is the really awkward
one. It is hardly geometry or physics in the ordinary sense ;
it looks like a mixture of pure convention and pure metaphysics. It has been traditionally formulated as $A = A$ or
A is A, wearing the innocent guise of pure tautology. This
formula is in fact the sole, authentic, 100% tautology. As it
works in practice the Law of Identity means that we take out
a general licence to say $A = B$ or A is B when we want to. It
is part of the doctrine of Substance or Essence. The one
empirical generalization we can be sure about is that no two
portions of experience are identical or precisely the same ; or
else they would be not two but one. Nevertheless we single
out certain similars and call them identical, or one and the
same. However hard we try we cannot stop doing it. Hume
did try hard but he could not. When he was repudiating
corporeal substance as having only fictitious identity he had to
presuppose a mental substance which possessed enough
identity to do the feigning. When he was repudiating mental
substance or identity he had to presuppose substantial or
identical ' impressions ' and ' ideas '. These are the skeletons

in the logical cupboard ; the question is whether it is better to parade them openly like the Aristotelians or lock the door and throw away the key, like most of the moderns.

This chapter is intended to defend Euclid against the charge of being out of date, and also to attack the view that there can be a science of pure form without content. This is a kind of hyper-Platonism that Plato would have scorned and that Kant, one would have supposed, demolished. It is also intended to point forward to the decisive step in observational science taken by Aristarchus and in experimental science taken by Archimedes.

CHAPTER IV

ELEMENTS OF ASTRONOMY: ARISTARCHUS

First steps · The spherical earth · Sun and Moon · Sizes and distances Methods of measurement · The Greek achievement

§1. GEOMETRY sprang from a technique of mensuration that in its early stages was easy, straightforward and quite respectable ; astronomy from one that was difficult and not always respectable. Compiling the almanac was always difficult whatever method was tried. Sometimes in some places the methods and aims of *Old Moore's Almanac* obtruded themselves. Even short range time keeping, such as mechanical clocks now perform, raised awkward problems. At any rate, men began to observe the stars carefully and systematically for the purpose of time reckoning. It would be absurd to deny the importance of the æsthetic appeal of ' the starry heavens above ' even for those who as yet knew little of ' the moral law within ' ; but it would be equally absurd to suppose that this would be enough to induce men to make accurate observations and keep careful records. The requirements of navigation were of no importance before the 15th century. For the short voyages of the ancients, who had no charts, the man who could identify the Pole Star or the Little Bear knew all the astronomy needed on board ship. Of course he had to watch the passing of the seasons to know when to lay up his ship before the winter storms, but that problem he shared with all responsible citizens, with farmers, priests and rulers, who also had to know the time of year.

Given the reliable Mediterranean climate, it is easy enough to know Winter from Summer, Spring from Autumn. The sun will tell you, the growth of vegetation, the movements of birds. They will tell you roughly, at least. The awkward question is : exactly how much of the season has passed ; how near are we to the next ? The phases of the moon might have been a good guide, had she been more reliable and less reluctant to perform the functions required of her. The lunar month does not fit exactly into the solar year, it is not even an exact number of days. Not only has the early astronomer to calculate with awkward fractions, but he has to discover them by measurement first. He does have more reliable indicators than the moon, namely the risings and settings of constellations and the changing positions of the sun among them. Even so, he finds certain irregularities among the stars, particularly the intriguing movements of the planets. The further he proceeds the more awkward become the fractions he has to calculate with.

By good fortune the Greeks in the earlier formative period had not heard Babylonian fables about the stars influencing human affairs ; or else they had the good sense to reject them. Unhindered by pseudo-science they could go ahead and produce the science of astronomy from the technique of time reckoning ; and astronomy so far as they took it, turned out to be applied geometry. The transition to science was not quite so simple as in geometry itself. Complete proof is not attainable ; little can be done at the early stages in the way of generalization. Astronomy is an observational science, but piling up more and more observations would by itself accomplish nothing ; and there was no genuine incentive at the beginning to do it. The superstitious incentive fortunately was lacking. The path of progress was first of all by *a priori* metaphysical argument. Had the Greeks been imbued with the doctrines of 19th and 20th century positivists the science of astronomy could hardly have begun and the pseudo-science of astrology might have come to stay. Astrology grew on a metaphysical foundation, but it could have flourished on positivist lines had the astrologer been allowed to predict events after they happened. This is perhaps a fanciful speculation ; the next point is less fanciful. Greek mathematicians were led, for internal technical reasons, to subordinate arithmetic to geometry, developing the methods previously discussed. These were the very methods which were required later for astronomy and later still for dynamics and physics generally. A pure science of arithmetic, even a generalized arithmetic like modern algebra, would have been little use to them compared to the geometrical algebra they had. The very superior technique of arithmetical calculation developed by the Babylonians would not have helped

much either. The Greeks abandoned arithmetic through
what was really a blunder, about incommensurables, and
because of their clumsy notation which made calculation
difficult. In their very blunders the Greeks were lucky, or
their genius turned even blunders to good use.

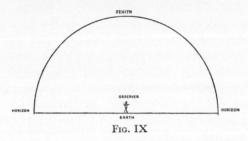

Fig. IX

The attempt to expound the earliest developments of Greek
astronomy is beset with difficulties, the evidence is so scrappy,
obscure and unreliable. Later writers whose work survives
just took the early stages for granted and never discussed them,
ignoring the troubles of future historians. Thus the future
historians have to do a great deal of imaginative reconstruction,
always a treacherous business.* However, one can be pretty
sure about the primitive set of ideas from which they started
and the conclusion arrived at by the time Aristotle wrote his
De Caelo (4th century B.C.). About some of the arguments
there cannot be much doubt. I shall first set out the chief
accomplishments as they can now be seen looking back over
two millennia. At the time they may have looked a bit
different, the parts we praise may have seemed unimportant
and things we think little of may have loomed much larger.

§2. The primitive observer finds himself in a world like the
sketch above. He is at the centre of a (roughly) circular disc,
the Earth, limited by the Horizon. Above him are the Heavens,
a hollow hemisphere with Sun, Moon and Stars imbedded in
it. Among the stars he distinguishes the Fixed Stars from the
Planets ; ancient writers often refer to Sun and Moon as
Planets too. His observations are of risings and settings ; of

* Translations of the relevant extant fragments have been collected in a very
useful form by Sir Thomas Heath in his *Greek Astronomy*, 1932. See also his
History of Greek Astronomy.

[53]

the time sequence in which they take place. The observer needs no instruments to begin with, and from risings and settings alone he can establish his chronology. But he can also observe the position on his (local) horizon where the various bodies rise and set. To do this he requires fixed points of reference, the beginnings of instrumental aids. Stonehenge, among its other functions, is supposed to have provided such an instrument, for fixing the summer solstice by observing the northernmost point reached by the rising sun on the horizon.

I must insist that what we *see* is exactly this primitive universe—flat earth, circular horizon, hemispherical heavens, discs or points of light rising in the east and setting in the west. At the present day so many town dwellers have never looked at the sky, but have read about stars in books and suppose the theories of the books to be observed facts, that this point needs to be insisted on. These are the facts as observed, the plain, true, correct, fundamental empirical generalizations. All the rest is theory or has theory woven into it. The sole defect of these facts is that they are local or parochial. Even that is not a defect for parochial purposes. When the Ordnance Survey construct their large scale maps, which take in one, ten, a hundred or perhaps a thousand square miles, they transfer their angular measurements and their linear measurements (reduced to scale) directly to flat sheets of paper, *as though the earth were flat*. In more refined language, they proceed as though the geometry of the earth's surface were Euclidean plane geometry. To introduce corrections to allow for the earth's curvature would mean a great deal of arithmetic done to no purpose, for the final result would be the same. When maps of the whole of Europe or of the Atlantic Ocean are being made, the method is different; but then that is not a parochial business.

As long as your concern is chronology alone and your interest is parochial a flat earth is all you require. It is only after you have spread your observations over a considerable area that it begins to fail. You find, for example, that on a night in the year when Canopus is well above the horizon at Alexandria, it is just on the southern horizon at Rhodes and invisible at Athens or Byzantium. Then you have to think again;

at least the earth is not quite flat. It is still a very long step from admitting that the earth's surface is slightly curved to asserting that the earth is a sphere. Indeed, the curvature can be *seen* in a quite definite sense, in the circular horizon at sea, in seeing the ship that has sunk below the horizon at sea level reappear above it on climbing a hill. In the first instance evidence from the stars does no more than reinforce this. The spherical form of the earth is not directly seen. The spherical form of a golf-, cricket- or foot-ball can be apprehended by touch, by handling it. Nothing the eye sees during the handling process or at any other time is strictly spherical. The earth is too big to handle. Perhaps that is just as well, but the consequence remains that its spherical form is theoretical. The theory is metaphysical in the simple sense that it depends upon distinguishing between appearance and reality ; between what is real, as being causally effective, though it does not appear, and what appears but is not quite so real, as being causally deficient or even deceptive. The distinction between appearance and reality is necessary but has always caused trouble. As Heraclitus put it, even Homer the wisest of the Greeks was puzzled by the riddle posed by certain little boys, who had been delousing themselves. The boys said : ' Those we saw and handled we left behind ; those we neither saw nor handled we bring with us. What are they ? ' (Diels, *Vorsokratiker*, Fr. 56.)

At any rate, when Pythagoras, or whoever it was, first suggested that the earth might be a sphere, he made the biggest, most risky, metaphysical jump ever made in the history of science. Modern developments in theoretical physics are metaphysical enough but child's play in comparison —not that they are easier to understand ; they are easier to make. The first step in the argument is to say that what we see is a fragment ; that there must be something complete beyond all parts, bounded, solid and analogous on its very large scale to the small bodies we handle. This may not seem a very big step, now in the 20th century, but it was in the 5th B.C. We may still ask : why make it ? A strict positivist would have to reply that there is no reason. He could point out that we never see the whole earth, so why should we suppose it to be a whole ? It does not look the least like the small bodies we handle, so why suppose it to be ' really ' like ? We only see bits, why not be content to talk about the bit we see ?

The second step is a more daring one. The Pythagoreans supposed the earth to be a sphere, mainly because the sphere is the most symmetrical and uniform of solid forms, the only one with no kind of irregularity or discontinuity about it. In the absence of any specific piece of evidence indicating a discernible and definable kind of irregularity or discontinuity none should be postulated. They knew that the earth must be so large that irregularities of the size of mountains were of negligible dimensions.

The third step (logically not historically last) is that the earth is not supported *on* or *by* anything. The notion of support is applicable to bodies on the earth to state their relation to the earth and is not applicable to the earth itself. This argument is the earliest known application of geometry to cosmology. It anticipates the Kantian argument about use and misuse of categories. It is also the earliest known use of Occam's Razor ; one of the few cases where this favourite metaphysical weapon of antimetaphysicians is useful. Evidence of a more empirical kind appeared later on to confirm the *a priori* argument. When qualitative observations such as those on Canopus (p. 54) were turned into measurements, systematically extended and the geometrical constructions implied in them completed, it was seen that a spherical form and no other fitted the facts. Of course, in its final form, the theory admits the qualification that the earth is very nearly spherical, not precisely so, by a few miles. This, however, is the result of positive, specific items of information, showing small but definite and systematic deviations from a perfect sphere (i.e. deviations from the simple rule which yet follow a rule). Experience goes further and further in the direction of making the spherical form apparent, but it never reaches so far. Experience goes further and points that way because the metaphysical jump was once made ; so the jump remains, though it seems to get smaller.

After a valid specimen of metaphysical argument it is only fair to mention one of the other sort. Astrology, so far as it is based on principles, is based on the analogy of Microcosm to Macrocosm ; an analogy that has little to recommend it in that form. Astrology also assumes that observed risings and settings of stars have some cosmological significance, not merely local chronological significance. This assumption is not compatible with the theory of the spherical earth. The long survival of astrological ideas shows how hard it has been for the spherical earth theory to make effective impact on ordinary human thinking, apart from technical astronomical thinking.

§3. Next, after the spherical earth theory came a more complicated piece of metaphysics ; the theory that Sun and Moon are also spherical bodies of measurable physical properties like the earth. This means that sun and moon are treated as *bodies*, and as if they were tangible whereas they are only visible. This means accepting all Euclid's Postulates, which are so useful on the drawing board and in the workshop where we can draw straight lines and circles, as applying to outer space, where we cannot. Anaxagoras' famous assertion which appeared very bold in his day and very modest later, that the sun is a very hot and very large body, at least as big as the Peloponnesus, marks the beginning of this line of argument. Epicurus' denial and his assertion that the sun is no bigger than it looks is the positivist, antimetaphysical reply.

If the sun and moon are treated as *bodies* and as though they were tangible then their sizes and distances are, in principle, measurable. It remains to work out a technique for making the measurements. This was the purpose of Aristarchus of Samos, whose treatise on *The Sizes and Distances of Sun and Moon* (3rd century B.C.) is the earliest complete and important astronomical work to come down to us. Beyond the theoretical assumptions already mentioned, Aristarchus requires three more : that the moon shines by light reflected from the sun ; that the moon is smaller than the earth ; that the sun is very distant and larger than the earth. Regrettably, Aristarchus assumes all this without argument. Even Aristotle, writing in the previous century, is not as explicit as he might be. However we can see well enough how the argument would go.

At each stage the argument uses analogy to go from the known to the unknown, from the part to the whole, assuming that the heavenly bodies are just bodies and their heavenliness not to be taken too seriously (*pace* Plato and Aristotle). As the visible form of the sun, and of the moon at the full, is circular there is no difficulty about supposing the ' real ' form to be spherical. If the moon shines by reflected light, then the observed boundary line between the lit and unlit portions at the various phases is exactly as it should be on the assumption that the moon is a sphere. The whole theory can be illustrated by simple experiments with a candle and a pumpkin. Notice that there are two independent hypotheses and if either were false the analogical demonstration would be inapplicable.*

Given that the moon is a sphere this dignity cannot be refused to the sun.† The next question about relative sizes is more complicated. First of all, the moon is seen to occult stars and, at a solar eclipse, the sun. No body is seen to pass in front of the moon, which is therefore the nearest of the heavenly bodies.‡ The next point is that the apparent size of, or angle subtended by, sun and moon are nearly constant and equal. Sometimes eclipses of the sun are total, sometimes annular, so the distances are not quite constant. It is clear that the moon is the smaller and nearer of the two. The third point raised the awkward question : why is the earth taken as intermediate in size between sun and moon ? The evidence comes from lunar eclipses (cf. Aristotle, *Meteorologica*, 345 b.). They can be explained on the assumption that the sun is larger than the earth, which therefore casts a conical shadow with its apex beyond the moon, but not very far beyond and certainly not reaching any other heavenly body. The moon is seen to be smaller but not much smaller than the width of

* After it was agreed that the moon shines by reflected light, some ingenious person suggested that the sun did so too. This hypothesis was soon dropped as no further and hotter and brighter source of light could be discovered. It was therefore superfluous. The story is interesting as showing how analogy tends to be pushed too far in the first flush of enthusiasm and needs checking by good sense.

† Cf. Aristotle, *De Caelo*, 291 b. ' If one body is a sphere others will be too.'

‡ No ancient observer seems to have seen a transit of Venus ; in fact they were not observed until predicted on theoretical grounds. Thus occulations by the moon, and, inferentially, by the sun were the only ones known.

the shadow where it passes through it. It is also seen that it passes through the shadow only occasionally, not at every full moon. The only satisfactory explanation of the eclipses is that the moon is smaller than the earth and not very far off, and the sun larger and much farther off. Experiments with a large source of light, such as a fire shining through a hole in a screen, and a pumpkin and an apple will illustrate the supposed state of affairs.

§4. Now we come to Aristarchus (Sir Thomas Heath, *Aristarchus of Samos*, 1913 ; referred to as H.A.). The first thing to notice about Aristarchus' treatise is that he sets out the argument in Euclidean fashion as though it were pure geometry —in a sense it is. He states very briefly the presuppositions he requires under the heading, *Hypotheses*. These contain general theoretical statements—leaving the reader to fill in some more ordinary ones for himself—and also the numerical data based on observation which he requires for his calculations. All the rest which follows is exact geometrical reasoning. There is no difficulty about the first three, the general theoretical statements.

They are (H.A. p. 352) :—

1. The moon receives its light from the sun.
2. The earth is in the relation of a point and centre to the sphere in which the moon moves.
3. When the moon appears to be halved the great circle which divides the dark and light portions of the moon is in the direction of the eye.

Then follow three in which Aristarchus sets out the numerical relations which he assumes to be observed :—

4. When the moon appears to be halved its [angular] distance from the sun is less than a quadrant by one thirtieth of a quadrant [i.e. $90° - 3° = 87°$]. Fig. X (i).
5. The breadth of the earth's shadow [at a lunar eclipse] is that of two moons. Fig. X (ii).
6. The moon subtends one fifteenth part of a sign of the zodiac [i.e. $30°/15 = 2°$].

The values of four variables have to be found, so that four equations are required. The fourth is provided by the implicit

E   [59]

premiss that the angles subtended by the discs of sun and moon are found to be about equal when the sun is eclipsed. Given these four values the rest of the treatise consists of the rather complicated argument by which Aristarchus arrives at the sizes and distances in terms of multiples of the earth's diameter. The argument is complicated because the trigonometrical ratios and the corresponding notation had not yet been devised.

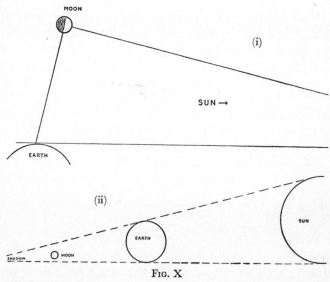

Fig. X

Before considering the conclusion of the argument some remarks on the data are needed. As to (4), the modern, calculated, value for the angular distance of sun and moon at the Dichotomy is $90° -10' = 89°50'$. It is hardly possible to measure this angle directly by observation because of the enormous optical errors involved. All measurements of distances of bodies in the solar system and the nearer stars outside depend on parallax—a shift in the angular distance of two bodies with a shift in the observer's position. The angular distance of two bodies can be measured very precisely when both are point sources of light, not too bright and of comparable luminosity. No precision is possible with large highly luminous bodies. Compare the failure of the 19th century

[60]

attempts to determine the sun's parallax by means of two transits of Venus with the success of 1930-31 observations on one of the very minor planets. Aristarchus' value was obviously a guess, and he probably took care to guess too large a difference from 90° so that his final result would provide minimum sizes and distances. Heath suggests that the actual numbers used may have been selected with a view to simplifying the arithmetic.

Hipparchus for his later calculation of the sun's distance used a more promising method (H.A. p. 341). At an eclipse of the sun in 129 B.C. when the sun was said to be exactly occluded at the Hellespont, it was occluded to the extent of $\frac{4}{5}$ at Alexandria ; this would give the sun's parallax directly and hence its distance, assuming that the moon's distance was known. The value of $\frac{1}{5}$ for the limb visible must be an overestimate ; but, of course, the optical errors are very large (see Abetti, *History of Astronomy*, 1954, pp. 287-89). Solar parallax cannot be directly determined with any precision. In fact the world has had to wait for indirect observations made in 1930 and 1931 to obtain the first precise calculation of the sun's distance, published in 1941 (Sir Harold Spencer Jones, *Mem. Roy. Astro. Soc.* Vol. 66, Pt. 2).

As to (5) the earth's shadow has a very indefinite edge, so that this figure cannot be made precise by observation. Hipparchus, later, put it at $2\frac{1}{2}$ and Ptolemy at $2\frac{3}{5}$. This last estimate is a trifle too large.

As to (6), Archimedes says that Aristarchus gave another estimate of $\frac{1}{2}°$, which is much closer to the right value. This was presumably a later estimate and the result of a definite method of measurement, probably of his own devising. The value $2°$ cannot have been more than a guess, and again as with (4) he chose a large value to give a minimum final conclusion.

Archimedes in *The Sand Reckoner* describes an instrument with which he measured the sun's angular diameter. He fastened a small disc to a long rod, pointed the rod at the sun, when on the horizon and not too bright to look at, and slid the disc along till it just occulted the sun. He then measured the angle subtended by the disc. He found the diameter to be less than $\frac{1}{164}$ and more than $\frac{1}{200}$ of a right angle, agreeing well with $\frac{1}{2}°$. (Heath : *Archimedes* p. 224).

It is clear enough that Aristarchus did not greatly care what the actual sizes and distances might be ; these were for him purely contingent facts from which followed no consequences, theoretical or practical. What he did care about was that in principle the estimates could be made so that he could say definitely :—Whatever the exact values may be, the sizes and distances of sun and moon *cannot be less* than the amounts calculated. That was in itself a result of the greatest importance, the first step in the direction of modern astronomy.

Aristarchus' and other ancient estimates are given below, from Heath (p. 350) :

TABLE

(All figures are multiples of Earth's diameter)

	MOON, Mean Distance	MOON Diameter	SUN, Mean Distance	SUN Diameter
Aristarchus . .	$9\frac{1}{2}$	9/25 (0·36)	180	$6\frac{3}{4}$
Hipparchus . .	$33\frac{2}{3}$	1/3 (0·33)	1,245	$12\frac{1}{3}$
Posidonius . .	$26\frac{1}{5}$	3/19 (0·157)	6,545	$39\frac{1}{4}$
Ptolemy . . .	$29\frac{1}{2}$	5/17 (0·29)	605	$5\frac{1}{2}$
Modern . .	30·2	0·27	11,726	108·9

The ancients attained a reasonable estimate of the size and distance of the moon for which relatively crude observation and Aristarchus' construction suffice. For the more difficult problem of the sun they had not the means, observational or theoretical. As has been mentioned, the sun's parallax cannot be measured directly with any sort of accuracy. However, given Kepler's laws and sufficient observations of the planets, a model of the solar system can be constructed ; then measurement of parallax of any member of the system (except the moon, which is useless in any case) will give its distance from the earth, hence the scale of the whole model, the radii of the orbits of all the planets and thus the sun's distance from the earth. In the 18th century it could be done roughly, at last in the 20th, accurately. Aristarchus' successors, except for Hipparchus whose contribution has been mentioned, had really nothing of importance to add. Posidonius' estimate of the sun's distance, according to the information provided by Heath, can hardly count as more than a lucky guess, fairly lucky but not quite lucky enough.

§5. Few ancient writers spent much time describing their methods of measurement, and Aristarchus, unfortunately, none at all. I have already said that his numerical values are little more than guesses chosen to give round numbers and a wide margin on the right side. I suggest further that when he wrote his treatise he had to all intents and purposes no instruments of measurement, and that it was this problem of sizes and distances that set him and others to devise instruments.

The problem of devising instruments is a most difficult one. From the time of Prince Henry the Navigator there was obvious need for an instrument for finding the altitude of sun and stars at sea, on a wobbling deck. This meant dispensing with plumb line or spirit level and measuring the angle between horizon and sun in one process, not two separate processes. A simple mechanical problem, one would think, and one which finally received a simple solution, the Sextant ; but it took two and a half centuries to find it. In these later times there was a strong incentive, urgent practical problems of navigation. There were also facilities ; skilled instrument makers trained in clock and watch making, and widespread knowledge of instruments and their working. The ancient world provided only a weak incentive—pure intellectual curiosity—and no facilities at all—no instruments, no craftsmen skilled in that kind of work.

We know of one early process of measurement which is sufficiently described and which also served to complete Aristarchus' argument ; that is to say, by measuring the diameter of the earth in terrestrial units it enabled his numbers to be converted into these units—stades, miles or kilometres. Rough guesses had already been made ; Aristotle (*De Caelo*) mentions 400,000 stades for the circumference, a considerable overestimate. It was a younger contemporary of Aristarchus,

[63]

Eratosthenes, who made the first genuine measurement ; and his method is described by Cleomedes (1st century B.C.) *
He noticed that at midsummer the sun was vertically overhead at midday at Syene in Upper Egypt (Aswan), indeed lit up the bottom of a deep well. At the same time it cast a shadow at Alexandria equivalent to an angle of $\frac{1}{50}$ of a meridian circle from the vertical. He took the distance between the two places as 5000 stades and assumed they lay due north and south. By a very simple geometrical construction this gives 5000 × 50 = 250,000 stades for the earth's polar circumference. Eratosthenes gave also a revised estimate, 252,000 stades, apparently to have a number more easily factorized. The

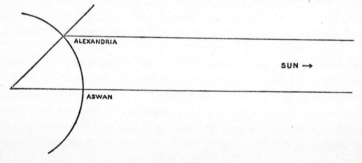

FIG. XI

Egyptian stade is reckoned as 516·73 feet and thus Eratosthenes' revised estimate would give a circumference of 24,682 miles and hence a polar diameter of 7850, only 50 miles short of the modern estimate. It was evidently a good estimate, but this very close approximation is accidental. Five thousand stades was a convenient round number based on day's journeys by camel or boat down the Nile, allowing for waggles. Eratosthenes and his contemporaries could not say more about the longitude of the two places than that they lay pretty nearly north and south. Lastly, there was an Attic stade and a Macedonian stade, as well as an Egyptian one, differing appreciably. Cleomedes in the same treatise (H.A. p. 345) gives an estimate by

* *On the Circular Motion of the Heavenly Bodies.* The relevant passage is quoted in the Loeb Edition *Greek Mathematical Works*, Vol. II, pp. 267 *seq.* See also H.A., pp. 109 and 147.

Posidonius based on observations of the star Canopus. Posidonius said that when Canopus was on the horizon at Rhodes its meridian altitude at Alexandria was $\frac{1}{48}$ of the zodiac circle, he gave the distance between the two places as 5000 stades due north and south and hence the earth's circumference as 240,000 stades. Apart from other errors, Posidonius' method is inferior to Eratosthenes', as measurements on bodies near the horizon are subject to large errors due to refraction by the earth's atmosphere.

Astronomical measurements began with rough judgments of equality and inequality and rough subdivisions by eye. Something more was needed if astronomy was to advance in the direction in which Aristarchus and Eratosthenes were looking, or even to go in any way beyond the purely local information provided by risings and settings. Once it is realised that the earth is a sphere, all angular measurements made on its surface at any place can be reduced to common terms, as though made at the centre. This is done by referring them not to east and west, local affairs, but to their altitude north or south and the time it is attained. A simple observation of the altitude of any star at the time it crosses the meridian provides all that is needed and makes the diurnal rotation of the Heavens (or the Earth) its own time keeper, a time keeper which has sufficed for very nearly every purpose up to the present day.*

Observation of meridian altitude calls for instruments. Whereas the geometrician could borrow ready made the instruments of carpenter and builder, his rule, square and dividers, the astronomer found none to do this new work. Aristarchus and his successors at Alexandria between them developed the instrument required, the Astrolabe. This still sufficed for Tycho Brahe. With Galileo's telescopic methods new instruments were called for, but essentially were modified forms of the astrolabe.

---

* It may be convenient to measure directly the angular distance between two bodies, one being a reference body whose position is known. This does not affect the principle here stated. Imagine the observer to be at the centre of a transparent earth, then the stellar map corresponds exactly to the terrestrial map in terms of latitude and longitude.

§6. The very first astronomical instrument was the sundial. Herodotus says it was introduced into Greece from Babylonia. Early dials consisted of perpendicular gnomons on a horizontal or vertical surface. These would suffice for rough measurements of the meridian altitude of the sun, such as Eratosthenes' measurement. Berosus, who came to Alexandria from Babylon in the 3rd century B.C., is said to have brought with him an improved sundial consisting of a hollow hemispherical bowl with a style projecting into the open circle terminating at the centre of the sphere. When held horizontally the bowl provides a reflection of the heavenly hemisphere and the shadow of the style gives direct and more accurate readings of angular positions of the sun and perhaps the moon. There is no evidence of further Babylonian developments. The next step in Alexandria was probably the making of an Armillary Sphere. This consists of a metal circle to represent the Equator fitted to another at right angles to represent the Meridian, and another set at the correct angle to represent the plane of the ecliptic in which the sun moves. The Armillary Sphere will have been intended in the first instance as a complete model of the heavens, with the earth at the centre, instead of a half model based on the flat earth view, such as Berosus' hemispherical bowl provided. It would soon be seen that the circles could be divided into signs of the zodiac, degrees or any other units. The model could then be used to take sights of the altitude of stars. Once the idea of taking a sight across the centre of a circle had been grasped, it was no great step to designing the Astrolabe. This is within its limits an instrument of precision and sufficed for the needs of astronomers for many centuries, in fact it sufficed for the discovery of Kepler's Laws. But, we must ask, for what purpose did the Alexandrians make observations? Nobody observes without a purpose ; there is no such thing as pure curiosity by itself, only applied curiosity. This does not mean that all purposes are utilitarian, only that there must be purposes.

They had solved one major problem when they had shown that the most conspicuous of the heavenly bodies were of determinate configuration, size and position. They still had to deal with the problem set by Plato, to find a geometrical construction to account for the observed motions, particularly the retrograde motions of sun, moon and planets relative to the fixed stars. There was also the old problem of the Great Year. These were seen as theoretical rather than observational problems and there was no strong incentive to record prolonged and meticulously accurate series of observations, such as there was after the fifteenth century. By the time Hipparchus had done his work (2nd century B.C.) the theoretical problems seemed to be solved as far as was necessary or possible. There were no practical problems, practical in the utilitarian sense, to disturb them. Failure to do something that badly needs doing forces itself on the attention. Even if it is only partial failure and the thing gets done in a sort of way, it may be still obvious that it is not done well. But small divergences between fact and theory are easily overlooked if nothing needs to be done about either. Practical needs without intellectual curiosity lead nowhere ; intellectual curiosity alone does go somewhere but not very far ; it is the two working together that really make things move. At any rate the successors of Hipparchus rested on their oars, content that wind and tide should take them.

§7. It is customary to think of the achievements, and failures, of the Greek astronomers in terms of the problem of Geocentric versus Heliocentric theory ; legitimately, provided its importance for them is not exaggerated. The solution of the problem really lay outside their technical resources and there was nothing to stimulate them to improve those resources. Quite early, Pythagoreans had suggested that the apparent diurnal rotation of the heavens might be attributed instead to a daily rotation of the earth. Aristarchus suggested the full Heliocentric theory (we do not know his arguments for it). However, as long as the question was discussed in geometrical or kinematic terms, and not in dynamic terms there was no real difficulty about geocentric theory, a stationary earth and rotating heavens ; it accorded with common sense and expressed the results of observation in a direct way. Astronomers had swallowed the paradox of the spherical earth

[67]

just to salve their metaphysical consciences, why swallow another ? Even supposing dynamical considerations are to be admitted, the weightless and frictionless heavens can surely be set spinning more easily than the ponderous earth and with less awkward consequences ?

True, the geocentric theory could not be maintained in its original and most attractive form as suggested by Eudoxus, in terms of simple concentric spheres. The geocentric theory did have to be a bit complicated, but the heliocentric theory held no great hopes of really drastic simplification. So Ptolemy argued, with the backing of the great Hipparchus. Nobody could possibly have anticipated the drastic simplification introduced by Kepler and Newton, whereby one set of laws suffices for all heavenly bodies (and terrestrial too) instead of a separate one for each planet. That came of abandoning circular orbits for elliptical ones. Had any Greek mathematician the technique which Kepler had for calculating orbits ? The circle is not only the ' perfect ' figure ; far more important, it is the only figure of uniform curvature with which calculation is relatively easy. Multiplication of cycles and epicycles did not make calculation impossible and could cope with the evidence pretty well. Its only disadvantage was that each cycle and epicycle was a new *ad hoc* hypothesis, and the whole Ptolemaic ' system ' was not a single system at all. It was a hotch-potch which did not solve Plato's problem—to produce *a* geometrical construction. It took Kepler and Newton together to solve that problem.

There is one point, though, to remember about Aristarchus which may be far the most important from the point of view of the future. As Heath suggests, Aristarchus saw that the sun is very much larger than the earth, and may have thought it more natural to suppose that the smaller moved round the larger and not vice versa. Then, taking the moon into consideration too, there was the beginning of a ' Copernican ' system. This means that we suppose that Aristarchus had some notion, embryonic though it may have been, of inertia, and hence took the dynamic view. But the dynamic view is not necessary ; it is possible to be resolutely kinematic. Then the question, which we are supposing Aristarchus to have asked, does not arise, and then it is easier to rest secure in our Ptolemaic slumbers. Still, if the heavenly bodies are to be treated as *bodies*, and not as illuminated points or discs, the question must arise sooner or later.

For most medievals and for very many very much later the earth remains flat and ' up ' and ' down ' stand for absolute divisions of space, not for relations between observer and earth's surface. An interesting example of confusion of flat with spherical earth theory comes in Dryden's *Annus Mirabilis* (1664) :—

> ' Then we upon our globe's last verge shall go
> And view the ocean leaning on the sky.'

Aristarchus' work on *Sizes and Distances* is classical, not for what he actually did, for he had no instruments, no observations in any strict sense of the word, only a geometrical construction correct but inapplicable. But the Greeks knew well enough that successful measurement is a matter of bracketing the thing to be measured between a minimum and maximum figure and narrowing down the width of the bracket by improving your methods until it is narrow enough. He could assign a minimum value at least. Having done that, he set his successors to work on the primary task of astronomy, to devise the instruments, carry out the observations and invent the methods of calculating the distances of the stars. Till 19th century spectroscopic methods came into use, it was practically the astronomer's sole task in addition to the direct mapping of apparent positions.

CHAPTER V

ORDER IN THE PHYSICAL WORLD

Platonic forms in nature · Precise or imprecise order? · Speculative imagination

§1. The original inspiration of Greek astronomy, as can be seen from Plato's dialogues, was the spectacle of the great cyclical regularities of the natural world—Night and Day—Winter and Summer—the Lunar cycle—the regular recurrence of eclipses. Here was ORDER writ large on the face of the universe, a guarantee that it was a Cosmos, not a Chaos. But the apparent order, however conspicuous, is incomplete. When the sun has run its course through the constellations and turns again at the solstice the repetition is not exact, because other bodies are not in the same positions they were in a year ago. The solar year is not a complete number of lunar months or even of days. Is there perhaps a Great Year after which, at a grand general solstice, all the heavenly bodies have returned to the same place exactly and are then prepared to repeat their courses exactly ; after 1000 or 10,000 or a still longer period of years ? This idea ran through most Greek thinking and lasted in one form or another almost till recent times. It was finally killed by the entirely new kind of mechanical synthesis of the 17th century, which made the *prima facie* regularities of terrestrial observation secondary and their completeness or incompleteness incidental. As a working astronomical theory the Great Year was abandoned long before, when the Alexandrians became aware of the Precession of the Equinoxes ; a small persistent shift of the sun's position in the signs of the zodiac at the end of each year. This meant that if there was to be a Great Year it would have to give time for the sun to work its way round through all the signs of the zodiac. It could be seen that this would take an immense time far beyond the possibility of computation in those days.

The Great Year question, though dismissed from astronomy, does raise in a simple and striking form a grave problem underlying all investigation of the natural world by observation. At the end of the Solar Year, let me repeat, say at the Winter

Solstice, when the sun turns back in its tracks to retrace its
course, other bodies are not in the same positions they occupied
at the previous Winter Solstice, the cycle is partial and incomplete ; there is no exact recurrence, only approximate
recurrence. Does that mean that the solar cycle is not genuine ;
not a real recurrence ; has no cosmic standing ; is, as we say
now, subjective, a human artifice, convention or myth, invented
as being convenient for certain human purposes ? Or can the
imperfections or deviations be disregarded as accidents or
somehow insignificant, so that the cyclic recurrence is real and
has cosmic significance in spite of them ? The plain alternatives are between Nominalism or Conventionalism on the
one hand and Platonic Realism on the other. For the moment
we may neglect later compromising theories, and stick to
Protagoras and Plato. According to the original Realist
theory the Form, Pattern or Law is an archetype, a kind of
cause. According to this view deviations from the Form can
be explained as due to the intractability of mere matter to the
imposition of form, in the same way that the carpenter explains
why his work is not exactly straight or square. It has been this
original Platonic or Pythagorean Realism which has been
operative among active investigators and practical men.*
Opposed to this view is that of the followers of Protagoras and
Gorgias, the critics and sceptics who never discover anything or
do anything, but are useful exploders of myths and superstitions dear to the heart of the practical man.

As long as we are thinking mathematically we can,
apparently, dodge the issue because we are not, apparently,
concerned with actual existents ; yet not entirely. In a
famous passage in the *Meno*, Socrates gets an untaught slave
boy to understand and enunciate a mathematical theorem by
questioning alone without telling him anything. Socrates
does draw a figure for him, first (i), then (ii), Fig. XII.

It can be seen from the figure that none of the squares in
(i) or any combination of them have half or twice the area of
any other. The possible numerical ratios of areas are 4, 9, 16.

---

* In spite of Whitehead, in his *Function of Reason*, (pp. 7 *seq.*) the wisdom of
Plato and the wisdom of Ulysses are closely allied. Ulysses in his more candid
moments is always a Platonic Realist.

But in (ii) the diagonals form a square which is half the area of the big square and twice the area of that smaller square whose side is half the side of the big square. The boy succeeds in understanding this on his own initiative—though after seeing the figure. A cat or a dog or a small child could see the figure equally well (we suppose) as far as vision goes, without arriving at any mathematical conclusion. Moreover Socrates did not need to draw the squares accurately, nor did the boy need to measure anything. Sensory intuitions mediate the process of understanding ; they do not provide the information asked for. That comes from the intelligence. So far there seems to be nothing to rule out the Platonic view that understanding is

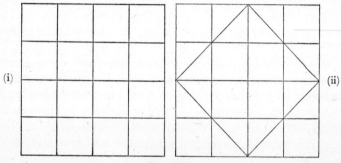

(i)   (ii)

FIG. XII

non-sensuous intuition. The sensory processes are incidental ; they might all have been different ; there need not have been any direct representation at all.— As Descartes said, you can reason about the properties of a regular chiliagon or myriagon, but you cannot represent it. Sensuous representation makes things easy, that is all. On this view the mathematical relation is ideal or hypothetical in the sense that it need not have any connection with any existing things—there are no regular chiliagons, yet the magnitude of the angles between their sides can be stated. The supposed Platonic form is here an archetype, not as imposing form on corporeal things to produce other existing things, but as a schema causing us to apprehend universal relations, though not itself universal. Our intellects are the ' matter ' on which form is imposed. Plato would hate to have it put that way ; so I must apologise for it.

All this is hair-splitting, abstract, high-brow stuff alien to the ideas of the plain man who distrusts reason unless embodied in imagination. If a builder, who can be assumed plain for purposes of argument, measures out on the ground a straight line 50 feet long from A to B, then another from B to C 50 feet long at right angles to AB, then from C to D another also 50 feet and at right angles in the same sense, he expects a fourth line 50 feet long to take him back exactly to A, or as near as he can judge, and so complete the square. If it fails to do so conspicuously, that is by several inches, he does not say that this is an imperfect world (hovering half way between Being and Notbeing) where the Forms are not fully exemplified. Nor does he say that Euclidean geometry is wrong, nor that space is non-Euclidean. He says he has not measured carefully enough and must try again. This he does until he gets it ' right ', as he says ; and then he stops. The practical builder believes that if he constructs a figure according to the Form of the square, then the Form must be exemplified ; it must be there because he has put it there. He may appeal to reason, with some justification, or he may appeal to experience, with rather less justification ; but it is imagination which tells him so. The most hard-bitten Nominalist or Conventionalist, if you catch him off his guard will say the same as the plain man. To that extent, in that special way, we are all Platonists.

The question about astronomical law would not be so difficult if it could be dealt with in the same way from a constructional point of view, on the analogy of human artifacts or machines. Thinkers of the 17th and 18th centuries did use that analogy ; wrongly, as most of us now say. But for the moment let us take it that way. A machine is constructed according to a specification, which is a sort of Platonic Form, determining (1) how it is to be made, (2) how it is to work and (3) what it is for. The specification is not complete without (3) the teleological part. In addition to all this the specification should state limits of tolerance, how much deviation is permitted from the exact rules laid down. This matter of tolerance is not a regrettable imperfection, but an integral part of design and workmanship. The designer who does not know how much deviation is permissible and how much is not, does not know

[73]

his job. The workman who tries to work more precisely than is specified fails to do his job as does the one who works less precisely. How widely or narrowly the limits are set depends upon the purpose of the machine and of each of the parts in the first instance, but secondarily upon conditions of manufacture which determine the degree of precision that can be economically attained. A clock that gains or loses a minute a day is quite good enough for ordinary household timekeeping ; it would be useless as a ship's chronometer. For the purposes of the first, wider limits of tolerance can be specified than for the second ; the first can be cheaply produced by mass production methods, which could not produce chronometers. To make clocks for household use to the specifications and by the methods used for chronometers would be wasteful extravagance and useless pedantry.

We can speak about machines in terms of archetypal forms without absurdity, and we can include in our terms deviations from perfect form ; in fact we have to. That is because machines are constructed by deliberation, for a purpose. Where no purpose is known, there is no deliberation, no construction ; what then ? In the 18th century they talked about cosmic clocks and clockmakers and thought themselves very wise. Now it all sounds like myth ; and not so morally instructive or picturesque as were more ancient myths. (20th century talk about ' chance ' and ' probability ' may be equally mythical, and 19th century talk about 'evolution' and 'natural selection '.)

The ancient astronomers, who were distressed to find that the order writ large in the universe was not perfect, hoped to be able to explain away the imperfections as merely apparent ; as due to taking a short or partial view. The ordinary solar year was imperfect, but the Great Year must be perfect. Suppose we had found that on 1st January A.D. 1800 every star (sun and moon included) was where it had been on 1st January 400 B.C. ; what then ? We could only say that the position was the same, within the limits of error of measurement, we could not say that further refinement of measurement would show no discrepancies. Suppose, which is more likely, that everything was more or less in the same place, but (say)

Moon or Mercury measurably out of place, though only by a small amount ; what then ? Should we say the 2200 years was not enough to complete the cycle and perhaps 22,000,000 years would do ?

Clearly the presence or absence of a Great Year makes no kind of difference to the actual solar year, which is actually observed. The turning and recurrence of the sun at the solstice is not to be dismissed as ' subjective ' or ' conventional ', on any theory, although incomplete in regularity. No completer regularity over a longer period makes that irregularity less irregular. We may consider the matter equally from the point of view of the primitive observer with a flat earth, from the Ptolemaic or from the Copernican point of view. At each Solstice a cycle has been finished and is begun again and is genuine, whether spoken of in terms of sun or earth. Order is still orderly in spite of accompanying disorder, provided of course there is not too much of the disorder. But how much disorder can we allow ? That is the awkward question. Apart from that question there seems little difficulty in maintaining a Platonic view of natural law in the physical world.

§2. I have begun this discussion in the most archaic, primitive terms to show that the problem crops up where men are doing no more than seek for *prima facie* order among phenomena, as positivists say we should always do. Astronomy developed along much more metaphysical lines as soon as the flat earth and hemispherical heavens were abandoned, but that did not greatly alter the problem, only the special terminology in which it was formulated. Whatever type of theoretical standpoint is adopted we still have to decide what to do about deviations from rule. Are we to abandon the rule, or stick to the rule and ignore the deviations, or assume that some more embracing rule can take care of both rule and deviations ? It is easy to see now that the search for the Great Year was a wild goose chase ; it may be less easy to see when similar geese are being chased at the present day. The value of a generalization is not always to be judged in terms of the degree of precision with which it describes actual facts. It may be concerned with an ' ideal ' situation never actually exemplified.

No projectile fired from a gun has ever described a parabola in its course. If any gunner laid his gun assuming such a course, we may be sure he would miss his target, except at point blank range where no kind of theory makes any difference. For all that, Galileo's law of the parabolic path remains the fundamental operative law in all theorising about ballistics and indeed in all practice.

As I have mentioned (Chapter IV, §7) a great defect of Ptolemaic theory was that it required a distinct *ad hoc* hypothesis and construction for each of the planets. The epicycles would not have troubled anybody had there been a uniform rule for them. Copernicus in his own day could offer no complete solution of the problem of the planetary paths, but he could introduce important simplifications and account for things that the geocentric theory left unexplained. Instead of referring the motions of the planets to the plane of the Equator and the plane of the Ecliptic, a vaguely defined plane inclined at an awkward angle to that of the Equator, he referred them all directly to one plane, precisely defined as that swept out by a straight line joining the earth and the sun. The orbits of Mercury and Venus were then disposed of by reference to the sun as centre ; that involved no great change. There were four defects in Ptolemaic theory he could make good at once. (1) It provided no criterion as to the relative distances of the various bodies, (2) no proper explanation of the stationary points and retrograde motions of the outer planets, (3) no explanation at all how Mars, Saturn and Jupiter were nearest the earth when in opposition to the sun and farthest when in conjunction, (4) the Precession of the Equinoxes was just sheer anomaly. Copernicus could deal with all these problems. He could not only place the planets in their correct order of distance from the sun, but make a very good estimate of the size of their orbits relative to the earth's orbit. The outstanding defect of Copernicus' system, as he formulated it, was that the sun was not the centre of the earth's (circular) orbit, and that he had to centre the other orbits in the same empty spot. It is not surprising that Tycho Brahe hesitated, sought for more evidence and so gave Kepler his opportunity.

Kepler's work besides overcoming this difficulty produced a

further simplification ; one set of laws for all the orbits (though he only worked it out in detail for Mars). And of course he could predict precisely as had not been possible before. Finally, Newton dealt with all orbits of all bodies of all sorts in terms of universal laws of motion and a universal law of gravitation, abolished special *ad hoc* hypotheses, and incidentally explained a host of hitherto unexplained and unrelated phenomena. It was the final answer to Plato's question : to find *a* geometrical construction to explain the appearances, not a hotch-potch of unrelated constructions. This last is an important point ; any theory will explain any facts as long as you are free to add on extra hypotheses to deal with new facts as they come along.

So far so good, except for a small fly in the ointment. The nearest of the heavenly bodies, and the most conspicuous after the sun, does roughly follow the Newtonian law. The moon's path, however, is not a tidy ellipse but a series of waggles roughly approximating to one ; and these waggles remain an intractable problem to the mathematician. The moon is too large and too near the earth for the simple Newtonian formula to apply directly, corrections have to be made, many corrections. For all that, everyone assumes *a priori* that *if* the mathematician could make his calculations he *would* find the actual path to be strictly Newtonian and all waggles strictly accounted for. We never assume anything else unless compelled to by the discovery of contrary facts which cannot be any longer explained away in the interests of theory. This usual assumption is one which only Platonists or plain practical men could make. Nominalists or Conventionalists ought to say that the Kepler-Newton scheme is a matter of conventions and artificial simplifications that happen to work very well for the orbit of Mars' or Jupiter's satellites, but equally do not happen to work well for the moon. They ought to treat it exactly as they treat the Great Year of the ancients or the Ptolemaic theory, which are more complicated therefore less useful conventions. If nobody does that it is because beneath a veneer of nominalism there always lurks a Platonist of the deepest dye when it comes to theories that have been learnt at mother's knee.

We must not be too hard on Nominalists or Conventionalists. They have a humble but necessary scavenging task to perform. They explode myths when these become too much inflated. They point out, correctly, that all symbols and other material of discursive thought and argument (if there be any other material) are artifacts and conventions in the first instance, and have to justify themselves before they are taken seriously. Conventions can survive only if they are convenient and artifacts if they are put together with genuine art. If they do survive then they are not so mere as they were once supposed to be. Every truth begins as a dream, as does every falsehood. Only time and more experience can tell us which dream came to us through the ivory gate and which through the gate of horn.

The primitive observer began by saying : ' The sun rose this morning between those two hills on my left and now is setting in the sea on my right.' He then saw that the terms ' right ' and ' left ' would convey false ideas to anybody facing the other way. Also, that for other observers a few miles away the sun would not rise between the two hills or set in the sea. He therefore had to find a more general framework of reference, so that any other person would understand correctly what he meant. He had to find certain technical dodges for leaving out of account the special position and circumstances of the observer—generalizing position and circumstances. This is a necessary preliminary to any generalization of the other sort— displaying the particular event observed at a particular time and place as an instance of universal order. The process is not correctly considered simply as making the observation ' objective ' or as eliminating the observer. All experience from the nature of the case has two poles, subjective and objective ; the observing on the one hand, its whence and when ; on the other what is observed, its where and when. The two are distinct but inseparable ; neither can be eliminated without eliminating the other. To make his report ' objective ' not ' subjective ' in the vulgar sense the observer has to put himself, as observer, in the right place (literally). It is no use Smith telling Brown he observes something unless Brown can place Smith, and the placing must be done in general terms so that it does not need to be worked out independently for each of Smith's observations, and Jones's and Robinson's not to mention Brown's own, when he is recording them, even for his own use.

For astronomy the main step in what might be called epistemic generalization was taken when all observations were referred directly to the earth's centre ; a process of reference carried out so easily with so little arithmetical fuss that it is hard to realise that there is a process at all apart from plain direct reporting of things seen. In a word, the geocentric report looks so like the egocentric report that few people notice the difference ; in principle it is vast. The ease of this process was the strongest argument in favour of geocentric astronomical theory. Heliocentric theory means recalculating observations at high cost in arithmetical labour. In the first instance it meant a great mathematical feat on the part of Kepler. He possessed a series of observations of successive visible positions of Mars relative to the fixed stars, angular measurements taken from the earth as centre. He had to translate them into the positions of Mars relative to the sun, so as to plot its orbit round the sun, although his point of reference, the earth, was assumed also to be revolving round the sun, so that he had apparently no fixed base line. The problem looks insoluble. Compared with these two steps, the first made by the Alexandrians, the second by Kepler, the efforts of the 20th century do not appear quite so marvellous. The whole process, though, has been the transition from a parochial to a more cosmic point of view. Whether or not a truly cosmic point of view has yet been attained is a matter of controversy.

The conclusions of the sciences of geometry and astronomy are stated in terms of topography and chronology, of spatial and temporal relations. Astronomy is concerned with actual events, though as exemplifying general laws. Geometry is concerned only with the kind of order that can be discerned in very nearly any event and not with one particular event in preference to another. Geometry is not concerned with quite all events, it does select, because its argument turns upon relations of inclusion and exclusion, equality and inequality,

whole and parts ; upon the law of excluded middle. When
we consider method, not conclusions, we find that these
sciences are not so exclusively chrono-topographical, but
nothing more needs to appear in theoretical statements or
conclusions. Indeed time can be reduced to mere succession,
can often be supposed to be reversible and spatialized as a
mere fourth dimension. For the purpose of control nothing
more can be asked for, since control consists in handling
artifacts by pushing and pulling. Understanding is a luxury
that can be dispensed with.

One further point : these two sciences aim at completely
general statements to arrive at which certain matters only are
taken to be relevant and all others are set aside. Therefore
their generality is highly specialized.

§3. Even at the earliest stages science requires the speculative
use of the imagination, and imposes a technical discipline upon
it, which it sorely needs and without which it may be absurd
and fantastic. But imagination remains free ; its sources are
outside the technical realm. Moreover it is only when
imagination can be specialized and applied to concrete cases
that this technical discipline is useful, and then its effect is
negative more than positive. Technical failure in simple cases
is definite and cannot be concealed. Technical success is far
less definite ; there are often a number of ways of doing
something in a sort of way, any of which can pass as success.
Though scientific endeavour as a whole succeeds by this
technical pruning yet many scientific practitioners are bad at
pruning their own extravagances. The lunatic fringe is not
absent even in scientific society.

Even in these most abstract and remote sciences so far
considered, the technical criterion is not the only one. The
æsthetic is there too, conspicuously in mathematics, which is
as much art as science ; but also, if less prominently, in
astronomy. Wherever collaboration in observing and recording
comes in, the moral criterion operates also, though behind
the scenes ; as I hope to make clear in later chapters.

Speculative imagination goes beyond or behind the
changing, discontinuous and incomplete that is found in

[80]

experience, in order to find or construct something stable, continuous and complete. It leads inevitably to cosmology, to a comprehensive world scheme. Cosmologies that profess to be scientific have been the projection of some human invention into the universe at large. The Pythagorean numerical cosmology is the first of them, quickly abandoned and now ridiculed; but not so ridiculous as many of its successors. The Great Machine theory of the world is equally and less legitimately a projection of human inventions. Historically it is pre-scientific, but Newtonian physics seemed to give it, at last, genuine scientific standing; and a great many people still believe in it, on sentimental rather than scientific grounds. The religious and moral approach to cosmology has often been no better than the supposedly scientific; it has too often been no more than the projection of human pride, greed, fear and folly into the universe at large. On the other hand Hebrew and Christian cosmology at its best has been free of these vices; it has been the attempt to see Nature, Man and God in God's terms and not in human terms.

Let us consider for a moment a very ancient almost universal cosmology belonging definitely to folklore, which had many attractions, but fitted ill with Hebrew or Christian thought because it was idolatrous; though that was overlooked for the most part. This was the Three-Decker Universe. (Chapter IV, Fig. IX.) It makes a strong appeal through direct sense experience to the simplest kind of speculative imagining. First, we see The Heavens over our heads, imperishable, unchanging, source of all light, warmth and goodness. Secondly we see, or rather surmise, beneath our feet The Nether Regions, haunts of darkness, death and demons. Between the two is the Flat Earth or Intermediate Region, where we enjoy life and the light of the Heavens for a little while before we pass Down, if unlucky, or Up, if lucky. This cosmology appears to harmonize our æsthetic and moral outlook with an actually observed physical order, based on absolute Up and absolute Down. The theory is idolatrous because, with its divine places and divine objects, it confuses the creatures with the Creator. It collapsed at the first touch of Greek astronomical theory, the theory of the spherical earth, which destroyed absolute Up and Down and should equally destroy divine things and divine places. However, traces of the theory persisted for many centuries. Cosmological poets clung to every scrap of it they could. Homer of course took it for granted. Plato should have known better, in fact did know better, but for his myths and images he needed absolute Up and Down, and divine places distinct from infernal places, with the human world in between. Virgil followed him, and Dante followed Virgil. Dante was a careful and accurate thinker and a conscientious Ptolemaist, but squeezed in all he could into his scientific framework. Milton followed Dante. He is said to have toyed with a Copernican setting for his poem, but it would not have done. The Copernican view admits no spatial priorities, all material things are equally material wherever they happen to be. No imaginative framework, no stage scenery for the drama of life can be built out of it. Note, however, that while Copernican theory destroys the old stage scenery it also destroys the idolatry which was implicit or even explicit in all cosmology derived from folklore. The poets' affection for the imagery of primitive cosmology was not frivolous or stupid. They all took a sacramental view of the universe, they saw all parts of it as bound together in a living order, each part reflecting the whole according to its kind. It is quite wrong to look for that order in the spatial arrangements of material bodies ; we are well rid of that illusion. But if the whole sacramental view of nature as related to man and man as related to God is lost too, then we have paid too high a price for the loss of a childish fantasy. I believe that there is nothing in any or all of the sciences, as now understood, to justify throwing away the sacramental view. Indeed there is much to help to restore it. But this postscript to the discussion of Greek astronomy is not the place to deal with it. (See Chapter X, §4.)

CHAPTER VI

ELEMENTS OF EXPERIMENTAL PHYSICS: ARCHIMEDES

Archimedes' methods · His concepts · The work on floating bodies · Specific gravities

§1. IN the history of the physical and exact sciences, if there is one man justly to be compared to ' the incomparable Mr. Newton ' it is Archimedes of Syracuse. Where others have excelled in one, or at most two, aspects of scientific activity they excelled in three : in mathematical invention or discovery, the excellence of the pure mathematician ; in the use of mathematical methods for the development of physical theory, the excellence of the applied mathematician ; in the actual manipulation of things for the purpose of scientific discovery or of utility, the excellence of the experimenter or inventor.

To single out Archimedes is not to decry Galileo or his work. Galileo turned from Statics to Dynamics ; a great step but the second not the first. He also described and explained his experimental method for all of us to understand. Archimedes, with that curious Greek prudery, kept the information for his special friends.

In mathematics Archimedes perfected a method which could do, though laboriously, the work of the Integral Calculus and used it with great ingenuity. In *The Sand Reckoner*, which might be taken as a mathematical joke, he showed that it was possible to devise an arithmetical notation to deal with numbers of any magnitude that could be suggested. This was an important contribution to thought in the Greek world, where arithmetical notation was clumsy and people were timid about large numbers. Incidentally, Archimedes makes the point that any physical aggregate which we can observe contains a finite number of parts. He considered the whole astronomical cosmos known in his day, making the most liberal possible estimate of its size, supposed it packed full of the smallest visible grains of sand and calculated how many grains there would be. The number of course was very large, but still finite and capable of statement. He argued in terms of the naked-eye cosmos of his day, but the argument is equally applicable to any astronomical cosmos and any constituent parts observed by any means however refined. By an amusing coincidence Archimedes' Cosmic Number is one of the same order of magnitude as Eddington's (cf. C. B. Brown, Archimedes and Eddington, *Philosophy*, 1940, Vol. 15, p. 269).

Of Archimedes' works on Mechanics those *On the Lever* and *On Centres of Gravity* have perished, but the third of the series, *On the Equilibrium of Planes* survives, also the work *On Floating Bodies*; enough for the foundation of classical mechanics. (Greek Mathematical Works, Vol. II, Ed. I. Thomas, *Loeb Class. Lib.*)

Before Archimedes there was a good deal of sound (and some not so sound) common sense information about mechanics, sufficient for technical purposes and often for high grade technique ; but very little that could be called science. In spite of that, or perhaps because of that, there had been a mechanical philosophy or metaphysics for nearly two centuries. It was more than metaphysics, it was myth, cult or religion, as can be seen in Lucretius' *De Rerum Natura*. Lucretius, though much later than Archimedes in date, is faithfully reproducing pre-Archimedean ideas. He is preaching a sermon, a good one within its limits ; he is not interested in science. Democritus and his followers, including Lucretius, maintained that all interaction in the world is by impact, without knowing anything about the laws of impact. These could not be known until the basic ideas of dynamics had developed and there could be no dynamics until the work of Archimedes had been understood and a number of further and difficult steps had been made.

§2. Aristarchus in his *Sizes and Distances* includes among his prior Hypotheses numerical data that are obviously contingent and empirically obtained. There is no contingency of that kind among the postulates of Archimedes' Statics. His treatment does rest upon common experience for the meaning of those terms that do not belong to geometry in general, but apart from that it is as pure and *a priori* as may be. His special notions of Equilibrium, Gravity and Fluidity refer back to common experience ; it is their necessary background, but they themselves are new, they are products of the creative imagination. In contrast, the fundamental notions of Euclidean geometry are products of common experience, as are those of arithmetic and logic. Because a notion is of that which is pervasive in experience, of what is everywhere, or nearly everywhere, and always, or nearly always ; and because it is very abstract as well as very general, it is not made thereby any more pure, *a priori* or non-empirical. What makes a notion such is that it is not merely found *in* or abstracted *from* experience, but created and *put into* experience by an imaginative metaphysical effort. These notions of Archimedes are to be compared with the Euclidean notions of parallels and of equivalent areas, or the astronomical notion of the spherical earth. Of course, once they are put in and experience is transformed by them they become empirical ; empirical by adoption not by birth.

All the propositions in Archimedes' Statics once formulated can be confirmed in experiment and the concluding ones are statements of what can be done by experiment. In that sense he should be taken empirically. Moreover he must have done some experimenting before he arrived at his postulates and process of argument ; exactly what we do not know.

In a Peripatetic treatise on mechanics of the late 4th or early 3rd century (Aristotle, *Minor Works*, pp. 330 to 411, *Loeb Classical Library*) there is useful, sensible discussion of problems connected with the properties of levers and on the whole clear understanding of those properties. (Incidentally, there is a clear statement of the Parallelogram of Velocities, which goes beyond ordinary common sense.) But Archimedes' notions of Equilibrium and Centre of Gravity are conspicuously absent. Indeed there is no proper distinction between the method of Statics and that of Dynamics. We can easily see therefore what is new in Archimedes' treatment. The rudiments of the notions of equilibrium and of centres of gravity come from the use of the balance in weighing and from observation of the positions of rest of symmetrical and asymmetrical bodies suspended from a point or otherwise free to move, as a wheel on its axis ; but ordinary inductive generalization from such observations provides no more than rudiments, if as much. The general notion of equilibrium and of centres of gravity applied to solids goes far beyond them and the notion of fluid equilibrium and equilibrium between a fluid and a floating body even further, so as to open up an entirely new realm of thought and experience.

Primitive common sense based on making and using tools easily acquired an adequate working notion of rigid bodies, but not much idea of any other bodies. Physical science followed common sense in this, so that right up to the end of the 18th century it was mainly a science of rigid bodies. The notion of a fluid is a more subtle and difficult one, that began to be full and precise in the 19th century. Even the elementary distinction between compressible and incompressible fluids had to wait for Boyle and his air pump—a concept often has to wait for a technical device. It is no great exaggeration to say that Archimedes invented the notion of a fluid ; it is no exaggeration at all to say that he first produced what was needed for scientific purposes. Archimedes is in fact dealing with incompressible fluids, for he assumes that there is a surface and that pressure is equal throughout the volume under equilibrium conditions, i.e. does not vary in a horizontal direction, nor significantly in a vertical direction in the gravitational field.*

The basic notions are those of a fluid in equilibrium and a rigid body immersed in it at or near the surface also in equilibrium with the fluid. That means that the upward pressure of the fluid equals the downward pressure of gravity. These are not simple or obvious notions ; they do not belong to ordinary experience or common induction from it. Everybody had known for centuries that wood floated in water and iron sank, and that bulk for bulk iron was heavier than wood. Somebody might have weighed a lump of iron first in air and then in water, and noticed that it weighed less in water ; but he would not have drawn any conclusion from the observation.

---

* Incompressible here is taken in the usual sense as meaning that only moderate pressures are being considered and under those pressures compressibility is negligible.

Without Archimedes' basic notions no conclusion could be drawn. The notions are related to the more nearly common sense or inductive notions of the equilibrium of the arms of a balance, but they cannot be deduced from or in any way analytically derived from them. Moreover Archimedes' notions can only be understood (not to say discovered) by the use of imagination. Any notation used in argument about them is subordinate to the imagination.

§3. To come to Archimedes' actual statement of his hydrostatic theory ; he makes two postulates, in addition to the general assumptions of Euclidean plane and solid geometry.

I. Let the nature of a fluid (τὸ ὑγρὸν) be assumed to be such that,
(a) of its parts which lie evenly and are continuous that which is under lesser pressure is driven along by that under greater pressure, and
(b) each of its parts is under pressure from the fluid which is perpendicularly above it, except when the fluid is enclosed in something or is under pressure from something.

II. Let it be assumed that, of bodies which are borne upwards in a fluid, each is borne upwards along the perpendicular through its centre of gravity.

There are two distinct postulates in I, which I have marked (a) and (b). The first is the statement of fluid equilibrium, or, as it might be put in modern terminology, the principle of equipartition of energy applied to fluids. The second adds the condition that the fluids to be considered are in a gravitational field. Postulate II then adds the principle of upward pressure operating on a solid, totally or partly immersed in the fluid ; and also the vitally important assumption that pressure can be taken as acting vertically through a single point, the centre of gravity. There are here four distinct notions and all that follows is the synthesis of them with the help of Euclidean geometry and its Archimedean extensions.

The key notion is that of fluid equilibrium, and it is, like the Euclidean notion of parallels, ' ideal ' not actually observed. Where motion is observed there is disequilibrium, but where no motion is observed there is not necessarily equilibrium.

A weight resting on an inclined plank is held in disequilibrium by static friction. A balance that is swinging is not in equilibrium. As the swings die down it is generally supposed to be tending towards equilibrium, but static friction may bring it to rest in a position that is not the equilibrium one. It is safer, and sometimes also quicker, to calculate the equilibrium position of the pointer from the extreme positions reached while it is still swinging. In doing this we see more clearly that to determine equilibrium conditions is a matter of theory as well as observation. We come nearer to direct observation in the easy case of the balance, than in the difficult case of fluid equilibrium, where we cannot see what is going on inside the fluid, but assume that there is nothing corresponding to static friction. As a concession to mythology, we may allow that greater insight is possible when the observer is himself immersed in the fluid.

Archimedes' postulates may be taken as definitions, though not as purely arbitrary, conventional or verbal. He is saying, ' I propose to discuss things having such and such properties in order to establish the logical consequences of their having them, and I shall not actually examine any of the things of that sort, but use models and diagrams to perform imaginative operations.' This is not to deny that there is an *arbitrium* involved and an element of convention and even of verbal definition, but to say that all these are subordinate and minor matters. It is on the other hand to assert that the argument is in its way as pure as any reasoning can be and also to deny that it is entirely formal reasoning ; indeed forms without content cannot be profitably reasoned about.

I have insisted that imagination is needed to apprehend the conceptual scheme involved and to understand the propositions and their proofs. This does not make the argument more or less empirical, or less or more *a priori*, but it does add to the difficulty of following it, for any diagrams used or any kind of notation are incomplete expressions and have to be imaginatively reinterpreted. The conceptual scheme is partly topographical but only partly ; so far as it is topographical, reinterpretation is at a minimum and offers little difficulty. For most Euclidean propositions and arguments, which appeal to the figure, direct sensory intuition suffices, but not for Archimedes' argument. There we need imagination that goes beyond just reproducing former sensory intuitions.

As to Archimedes' actual argument it must suffice to mention three important conclusions.

Prop. 2. The surface of any fluid at rest is the surface of a sphere having the same centre as the earth.

The proof is by *reductio ad absurdum* and depends upon the symmetry of a spherical surface. The proposition is general, applying to any spherical body having a gravitational field, so that the empirical fact that the earth's surface is spherical is strictly irrelevant. Archimedes need not have mentioned the earth ; it is a concession to the reader's desire for concrete illustrations. Of course if you are introducing empirical considerations, it is a fact and a very important one that the nearest we can get to observing a spherical surface on a large scale is to observe the surface of the sea ; and the sea is a fluid at rest and in equilibrium, or nearly enough for the purpose of the argument.

Prop. 7. Solids heavier than a fluid will, if placed in the fluid, sink to the bottom, and they will be lighter (if weighed) in the fluid by the weight of a volume of fluid equal to the volume of the solid.

This is the law of Specific Gravities and the theoretical basis for Archimedes' celebrated solution of the problem of the crown : to discover without destroying the crown whether the gold of which it was made had been adulterated. In doing this Archimedes reached, incidentally, the basic theoretical conception of chemistry (and the refutation of alchemy). That is that there are substances with specific properties, e.g. gold and silver, and that everything else which is not a pure substance is a mixture of substances with intermediate or mixed properties, e.g. an alloy of gold and silver. But this idea lay dormant till the 17th century ; though it was implicit in ancient atomic theory (cf. Lucretius, *De Rerum Natura*, I, ll. 635 *seq.*).

In the second book of his treatise Archimedes works out a number of propositions on the conditions of stability and instability of floating solids of certain general forms, namely paraboloids of revolution, bodies whose vertical cross section in any plane is a parabola. These bodies are selected because he has already worked out their geometry, particularly as to their relations of symmetry and centres of gravity. In effect, however, Archimedes discusses in an idealised form the lateral stability of ships, whose cross section approximates to a parabola (though no ship is of uniform density throughout its cross section). Still, the fundamentals are there, showing that under certain conditions the downward pressure of gravity and upward pressure of the water provide a ' righting ' force and in others a ' capsizing ' force ; and that in general, stability is attained by keeping the centre of gravity low and the centre of pressure high. In the 3rd century B.C. this conclusion did not sound so platitudinous as it does in the 20th A.D.

§4. The law of specific gravities Archimedes could and, according to our authorities, did apply in practice. There are no obstacles in the way of the experiment, no technical difficulties, and actual conditions can easily be made to approximate to ideal conditions. Whether he gave advice to the shipbuilders of Syracuse, or whether they took it we do not know. In that case the application of theoretical principles is not so easy. The question of whether or not Archimedes applied his theory is not an idle one. Whatever may be the truth about 20th century physical theory, the truth about classical physical theory is that practice and theory were indissolubly wedded. If they are now divorced, as some people think they are, that is to be regretted.

Classical theoretical concepts belong to an ideal world of simplified operations, but operations of experiment, which belong to an artificial world as near the ideal as possible. Nevertheless they are both rooted in common experience however far they have grown out from it. As Euclid's concepts are related to those of the Egyptian cord-stretchers, so are Archimedes' to those of the merchant weighing his goods on the balance (the honest merchant with an honest balance), and rather more distantly the shipwright who endeavours to make his ship seaworthy. The knowledge of the ordinary man and more specially the ordinary craftsman is the ultimate basis without which there would be nothing at all. But by itself it does not go far enough to make a science ; that requires theory.

Everybody knows that wood floats and iron sinks in water, and everybody knew it for centuries before Archimedes. Centuries after him, through ignorance of his work, nearly everybody said that a ship built with an iron hull would sink. Moreover nobody else could have hit upon the ' obvious ' solution of the problem of the crown. Plain inductive generalization from ordinary common experience provides answers that are right for the most part, but sometimes are wrong and often it provides no answer at all. Against this, theory and experiment together provide answers which are right every time—under certain conditions. Theory gets beyond mere contingency and introduces an element of necessity—under certain conditions. The qualification means that theory deals with a simplified ideal system and experiment tries to reproduce it closely enough to avoid error or doubt.

Take a piece of steel of convenient and regular shape, say a cube or sphere, weighing $7\frac{3}{4}$ lb., then cut out pieces of brass, ebony, oak and white pine of the same volume ; they will be found to weigh about $8\frac{1}{2}$, $1\frac{3}{4}$, $\frac{3}{4}$ and $\frac{1}{2}$ lb. respectively. Suspend them in water, and the steel, brass and ebony will be found to weigh 1 lb. less. The oak and pine will weigh nothing at all as they will float, but it will be seen that the oak floats with about $\frac{3}{4}$ of its volume submerged, the pine with about $\frac{1}{2}$. These results of experiment are expressed in the future tense to indicate that the figures are taken out of the book and not from observation, and also to indicate that if anybody's observation contradicted the book we should all still trust the book and distrust the observation.

The figures given are not very precise and to that extent there is doubt about them. They can, however, be made much more precise and that sort of doubt greatly diminished. They are not precise because the common materials named vary in composition, and the conditions of weighing may vary, particularly in respect to temperature. But we can specify materials and conditions carefully and in detail, so that pure substances are weighed under well controlled conditions ; then our predictions will be fulfilled very precisely. The greater the care in specifying and the greater the care in carrying out the observations the greater will be the precision with which prediction from theory is fulfilled. That is because we shall have created an artificial system to correspond to the ideal system of theory, and then there will be an element of necessity about the business which is sadly lacking in the raw, natural world. No physicist, I venture to claim, will accept the conclusion that the density of pure iron is $7\cdot87$ *for the most part* but not necessarily. If anybody claims to find a different density we say the iron used was impure or the conditions of weighing were not as specified ; the observation was a lapse into the raw, natural world. Unless observation agrees with theory always and not just sometimes there can be no stable theory. Some physical theory is stable, not tentative nor liable to change, though it is always of an old, humdrum, inconspicuous kind. All the more ' high falutin ', conspicuous kinds of theory are tentative and speculative and liable to change or even to be discarded completely as new facts emerge, but all such theories are luxuries, not necessities, and that is why they are so much talked about. The kind of theory Archimedes was concerned with is necessary in both senses ; there is nothing tentative about it ; to change it would be to destroy the whole of physical science.

The kind of necessity I am here concerned with has not generally been recognised because of the tradition that there is only one kind of necessity, that of valid deductive inference, and that there is one other kind of inference only, namely inductive, which gives no more than probability. If theory were purely formal and fact purely contingent the traditional assumptions would be good enough, but then there would be no kind of connection between fact and theory, and of course no science. For what makes physics a science is that its theory is not purely formal and its experimental facts not purely contingent. Its theoretical concepts arise out of common technical practice and give rise to new technical practice that is more powerful and much more precise. In a word, the theory is a theory of the behaviour of things as handled.*

* This does not contradict the assertion that things handled are artifacts. It means that artifacts are properly constructed of real stuff.

One further point ; physical laws can be expressed in the form—*Under such and such conditions, so and so will happen.* They are then subject to the proviso—*Provided nothing interferes.* In that sense all laws are contingent and hold only for the most part. Properly conducted experiment is the attempt to stop things interfering, so that if things do interfere the experiment is discredited rather than the law. Therefore there is the other sense in which well substantiated laws are necessary and universal ; they are assertions of the existence of order. (They are still assertions of order even if it is large scale statistical order arising out of small scale chaos.) Occasional experimental failure involves the admission of chance in that instance, just as the irreducible random errors of observation involve the admission of chance, but not in a way which contradicts the assertion of order. Human control is limited in many different ways and the notion of contingency expresses one of the aspects of that limitation.

CHAPTER VII

FROM ALCHEMY TO EXPERIMENTAL CHEMISTRY

True and false beginnings · Origins of alchemy · Alchemy in Berkeley and Newton · Chemical substances · Chemical analysis · Atomic theory · Large molecules · Biological implications

§1. The Greeks did a great deal, did it very well, and we have profited ever since from the legacy they left us. Their legacy was, however, lop-sided, and no more complete than anything else in human affairs.

It is clear that the Greeks put too much faith in mathematics, in the *a priori* aspect of knowledge and in general concepts akin to the mathematical. Aristotle's method of overcoming the tendency to mathematicize was equally *a priori* and not successful. You cannot force teleological or any kind of biological concepts on to physics without the risk of spoiling physics. Every science or branch of investigation is autonomous ; it must find its own concepts, in its own field, by its own methods. Of course, this principle of autonomy must not be run to death. There are interrelations between sciences, there are common concepts, there is the proper and necessary use by one science of external concepts which may be borrowed from another. Teleological concepts must not be forced onto physics ; that does not mean that physics cannot use them. The physical use of the concept of *efficiency* shows that it can. Also, the autonomy of one science should not be used imperialistically to destroy that of others. Concepts should be employed up to their proper limits but never beyond them.* All these dangers of abuse of autonomy are now seen. In the early days they were not seen, but the dangers of abuse were remote, and it was recognition of autonomy that was most needed.

In Aristotle's day and even much later the character of mathematical and quasi-mathematical concepts was ill understood. The concepts had been acquired too easily, without

---

* This may sound platitudinous, but it has been neglect of such platitudes which has led to the opposed errors of Hegelianism and Positivism, to mention only two instances.

enough examination, from common technical method ; they were a modest, almost unspoken, unrealised part of folklore. Because of this nobody saw that care and hard thinking are needed to acquire workable concepts and a workable classificatory scheme. Classifying is not to be done in the cavalier fashion which seemed possible to Plato and Aristotle. If these great men treated it in cavalier fashion lesser men failed to treat of it at all. It is true enough, as Descartes says, that when at first you cannot find a natural system of classification you should start with an artificial one. But equally you must realise that it is artificial and alter or discard it before it gets in the way. If you are lucky enough to find a valid classificatory scheme ready made, it is a help at the time even if there is a price to be paid later. Chemistry and biology had to arrive at their basic concepts and classificatory schemes with toil and difficulty ; the former entirely in post-Hellenic times, the latter mainly.

Chemistry in its early days was not helped at all by the well developed mathematical and physical sciences, and was hindered by folklore and equally by more sophisticated metaphysics. There was in fact no science of chemistry in spite of the pioneer work of Boyle, until the late 18th and early 19th centuries. It began in a serious way with Black, Cavendish, Priestley, Scheele and Lavoisier. Positive concepts had to be produced out of nothing, and rubbish had to be cleared out of the way. Theory was not free of confusions nor firmly established till Cannizaro cleared up the mess in 1853. Then the work of the early analysts bore fruit, the chemical compounds could really be described and classified, because at last Avogadro's correction to Dalton's atomic theory was accepted. The history of chemistry belies the common view that there is at first a dull, easy, classificatory or natural history stage which can be forgotten, then comes theory and all the interesting and difficult part. Instead it was the beginning that was difficult, and in its way very interesting ; classification and theory came together, each one necessary to the other.

The history of biology is different in many ways, but it also illustrates the interrelation of theory and ' natural history '. Biological concepts, so far as any have yet been acquired, have come more gradually and easily. Folklore has been more helpful and metaphysics no hindrance. There has been rubbish to get rid of, but with two exceptions mentioned below, incidental rubbish. The fable of the Barnacle Goose did not prevent people from recognizing and correctly describing the mode of reproduction of the Domestic Goose. The pleasant fancy of the Swan song did no more harm in its day than has the Loch Ness Monster in ours. Still it has to be remembered how late have been important turning points, which mark, not the continuation of the science on new lines, but its very beginning. The middle of the 19th century is perhaps the crucial turning point. Two things happened. Darwin published *The Origin of Species* in 1859, which settled temporarily the great problem of the systematist ; could his classifications be considered as natural or genetic, not purely artificial ? It left a lot of loose ends and led to much metaphysical speculation, and even more parametaphysical speculation—if I may be allowed this term to cover the kind of thing commonly mistaken for scientific philosophy. At about the same time Pasteur showed that the traditional theory of spontaneous generation was baseless, and in virtue of the opposed theory of biogenesis instituted microbiological methods, which have revolutionized both pure science and technology.

However, we must deal with chemistry first. It deserves treatment in some detail as providing a contrast to the fortunate sciences which acquired autonomy and their own proper concepts easily and early. Chemistry started as Alchemy, one of the two great scientific frauds of ancient times. The other one, Astrology, is so completely fraudulent as to be uninteresting, except for the single point that it illustrates the misuse of metaphysics. Astrology depends upon a special interpretation of the theory of the relation of Microcosm and Macrocosm, which theory is itself a special interpretation of the theory of The Great Chain of Being. Astrology was a case of misuse of metaphysics, not necessarily bad metaphysics, and it never had a shred of empirical evidence in its favour or any genuine technique.

[96]

§2. Alchemy also derives from The Great Chain of Being in a different and far more instructive way because for all its bogus claims it never rested on pure illusion, it embodied some genuine chemical technique. In fact there was a great deal of genuine technique, all the methods of preparing and handling chemical substances, other than metals, originated in the practice of the alchemists. In contrast, no horoscope ever drawn up ever predicted anything except by chance, and as the technique of drawing them depends upon risings and settings of stars it is obviously a sham, once the flat earth theory and Three Decker Universe are abandoned.

The history of alchemy raises an intriguing question. Could chemistry have developed directly and honestly, without this preliminary phase of illusion and fraud ? Was it just bad luck that it happened to start off in the wrong way, with the wrong kind of intentions and with metaphysical illusions ? Or was it a necessary process by which errors had to be worked out in order to be seen to be erroneous before a fresh start could be made without them ? I am inclined to support the last suggestion. In many cases heresy is the price to be paid for orthodoxy. If there are conspicuous, easy ways of going wrong, then they must first be pursued with conviction until it is seen that they are wrong, otherwise it will never be seen. Until somebody takes a false hypothesis seriously it cannot be seen to be false. Nevertheless some sixteen centuries were spent working through the fallacies of alchemy ; and that is a very long time.

The idea of The Great Chain of Being sprang directly from ancient folklore and seemed the obvious kind of metaphysics in the ancient world, and indeed until the much worse metaphysics of The Great Machine began to displace it in the 17th century. In the ancient world the atomists alone rejected it. Their mechanical philosophy might perhaps have done something to create chemical concepts and methods. In fact it did nothing, for circumstances were against it. It was unpopular. After the 5th century it was upheld and expounded by Epicureans only and not for any scientific purpose. They were not interested in science, but in morals, and used it as a weapon to attack popular religion and related moral ideas.

Even in the hands of exponents with scientific interests, like Democritus himself, it is doubtful whether anything could have been done with it in the 4th or 3rd centuries B.C., seeing that the atomic theory had still no necessary place in the science of Galileo and Newton, and had to wait for the 19th century to come into its own. Then at last the time was ripe.

True, there is a natural and easy deduction from atomic theory of which we find signs in Lucretius' *De Rerum Natura* (I, ll. 635 *seq.*), namely the chemical notion of substances with distinct and specific properties. If we were to examine bodies consisting entirely of one kind, then the body in bulk would be found to display unalterable and specific properties corresponding to those of the atoms. This deduction could not be useful, however, while there was no way of finding such pure species of bodies. Certainly the traditional ' roots ' of things, earth, water, air, fire * did not look like ' elements ' of the chemical kind for their properties were not specific and they appeared to be transmuted freely. In fact the singling out of these four ' roots ' provided a large part of the empirical argument for transmutation. It was not until the 17th century that Boyle, an atomist by metaphysical conviction, pointed out that gold or silver has a better claim to be an elementary substance than these ' roots '. But he said it in the light of empirical knowledge that was not available in antiquity ; knowledge attained by techniques which were the fruit of centuries of alchemical practice.

Archimedes apparently had grasped the point, if nobody else had. His method of testing the king's crown for adulteration of the metal was based upon the assumption that gold, silver, copper and other metals were substances with specific properties. But his method was immediately useful for gold only, not for other metals, and certainly it was not exploited. Atomism was barren where it might, possibly, have been fertile ; the rival philosophies had it all their own way. That way led Platonist, Aristotelian, Stoic or plain folklorist to The Great Chain of Being, and so to Alchemy.

---

* The term ῥιζώματα used by Empedocles (Fr. 6 in Diels *Vorsokratiker*) is less misleading than στοιχεῖα.

§3. This theory of The Great Chain of Being, need not be taken in its full Leibnizian form as embodying the doctrine of ' plenitude ' ; namely that in the hierarchy of forms all compossible forms are actually exemplified, so that there are no gaps in the natural order (cf. A. O. Lovejoy, *The Great Chain of Being*, 1942, pp. 52 *seq.*). Indeed empirical evidence at all levels, primitive and advanced, is against this doctrine. If it were true no distinctions of kinds would be discernible, because all possible intermediate gradations of form would be present everywhere. The idea of a complete qualitative continuum is a metaphysical nightmare, best forgotten. The usual doctrine of The Great Chain was more moderate, plausible, indeed almost entirely reasonable. It was nothing more extravagant than the view that all things are interconnected, that there is one universal substratum or raw material out of which all things possessing form (and therefore recognizable, classifiable, utilizable) are made, by an active process of ' informing ' (analogous to human manufacturing) ; that all processes of composition and decomposition, growth and decay, of being born and dying are of this kind ; that all forms can be graded as more perfect or less perfect ; that the primal and universal activity is spiritual, akin to life in all its manifestations, and that fire is a kind of life. This last clause, about fire, is a bit extravagant ; the last but one, about spiritual activity, needs more cautious interpretation than it usually got ; but otherwise there is nothing very objectionable about the theory. It is offensive to the dogmatic materialist, but that is rather in its favour than against it. It does not necessarily raise any difficulties for any branch of science. It does, however, because of its use of sweeping analogies, open the way to possible extravagances. So after all does The Great Machine metaphysics.

In Berkeley's *Siris* (1774) * we find the doctrine of The Great Chain and alchemical doctrine too. Berkeley was an eminently sane and practical minded man, though a bit old-fashioned in opposing the prevailing mechanical philosophy

---

* Specially §§ 29 *seq.* For a fuller account see my paper in *Proc. Brit. Acad.*, 1954, Vol. 40, p. 41. The question how far *Siris* marks a change in Berkeley's views is there discussed.

with a philosophy of the previous century. His tar-water was, for its time and circumstances, a useful household remedy. It was very cheap, easily prepared by any housewife, a mild antiseptic that could be applied externally or internally ; it would do good in quite a number of common ailments, and could hardly do much harm in any. In all these respects it was definitely superior to most of the remedies then prescribed by the Medical Profession. The only contemporary complaints against tar-water came from disgruntled members of the Profession, who accused Berkeley of being a blackleg and taking the bread out of their mouths. (They need not have worried ; for most patients prefer medicine to be expensive, nasty and mysterious ; at least, nastier than tar-water, which was made from wood-tar, not coal-tar.)

According to the argument in *Siris*, as for Platonists and Aristotelians generally, there is no such thing as mere lifeless inert matter, and no causation can be merely mechanical. For anything to come into existence and possess any definite character it must be in some degree informed, transformed or animated by soul or spirit, and according to that degree has its place in the hierarchy of forms of greater or lesser perfection. The result of this view is that lower is seen in terms of higher ; animal life on the analogy of conscious life, vegetable life on the analogy of animal. Nothing can be said against this view in general ; but analogies should be used with caution and not too far ahead of empirical evidence. It can be said against those who used the same kind of argument, that they did run ahead of empirical evidence and were not cautious. The same accusation can be made against the upholders of The Great Machine philosophy of the 19th century. On the whole The Great Machine is sillier and gives rise to more pernicious superstitions than The Great Chain of Being.

However that may be, according to *Siris* vegetable life is analogous to animal life. It is claimed that a vegetable soul or spirit is preserved in tar-water which can operate bene-ficially on the animal and human organism. This active vegetable spirit is said to come in the first instance from the light of the sun and is specially abundant in resinous trees from which the most potent tar is made. The atmosphere of thought here is alchemical. It is totally contrary to 19th and 20th century mechanical philosophy, which is imbued with chemical theory, but not to the earlier 18th century mechanical philosophy. The Newtonian philosophy had nothing to say against it ; Newton himself expressed alchemical ideas in one of the last things he wrote for publication. In Questions 30 and 31, added to the 1717 Edition of his *Opticks*, he discusses chemical problems. It should be mentioned that Newton devoted at least as much time and trouble to chemistry as to physics, if not much more. It is possibly not necessary to mention that Newton had an alert and critical mind and was not without knowledge and skill in scientific matters. He might have been sceptical about the virtues of tar-water, but he would not have dismissed Berkeley's line of argument as absurd, and he had no kind of objection to the theory of The Great Chain of Being, with which he had long been familiar from More and Cudworth. It is perhaps best to quote Newton's Question 30 at length :—

" Q.30. Are not gross Bodies and Light convertible into one another, and may not Bodies receive much of their Activity from the Particles of Light which enter their Composition ? For all fix'd Bodies being heated emit Light so long as they continue sufficiently hot, and Light mutually stops in Bodies as often as its Rays strike upon their Parts, as we shew'd above. I know no Body less apt to shine than Water ; and yet Water by frequent Distillations changes into fix'd Earth, as Mr *Boyle* has try'd ; and then this earth being enabled to endure a sufficient Heat, shines by Heat like other Bodies.

' The changing of Bodies into Light, and Light into Bodies, is very conformable to the course of Nature, which seems delighted with Transmutations. Water, which is a very fluid tasteless Salt, she changes by Heat into Vapour, which is a sort of Air, and by Cold into Ice, which is a hard, pellucid, brittle fusible Stone ; and this Stone returns into Water by Heat, and Vapour returns into Water by Cold. Earth by Heat becomes Fire, and by Cold returns into Earth. Dense Bodies by Fermentation rarify into several sorts of Air, and this Air by Fermentation, and sometimes without it, returns into dense Bodies. Mercury appears sometimes in the form of a fluid Metal, sometimes in the form of a hard brittle Metal, sometimes in the form of a corrosive pellucid Salt call'd Sublimate, sometimes in the form of a tasteless, pellucid,

volatile white Earth, call'd *Mercurius Dulcis ;* or in that of a red
opake volatile Earth, call'd Cinnaber ; or in that of a red or white
Precipitate, or in that of a fluid Salt ; and in Distillation it turns
into Vapour, and being agitated *in Vacuo*, it shines like Fire. And
after all these Changes it returns again into its first form of Mercury.
Eggs grow from insensible Magnitudes, and change into Animals ;
Tadpoles into Frogs ; and Worms into Flies. All Birds, Beasts
and Fishes, Insects, Trees, and other Vegetables, with their several
Parts, grow out of water and watry Tinctures and Salts, and by
Putrefaction return again into watry Substances. And Water
standing a few Days in the open Air, yields a Tincture, which
(like that of Malt) by standing longer yields a Sediment and a
Spirit, but before Putrefaction is fit Nourishment for Animals and
Vegetables. And among such various and strange Transmutations,
why may not Nature change Bodies into Light, and Light into
Bodies ? " (Newton, *Opticks*, pp. 374-5, Ed. 1931 (Bell).)

Newton is more sober and factual than the general run of
alchemists, but the ideas are theirs. Moreover apart from
details about mercury and its compounds and the use of the
term ' salt ', it might have been written by Aristotle. If all
qualitative change is thought of in terms of growth and decay
as they are seen in the animate world—the obvious common
sense way of thinking—then they must be thought of as
transmutations. The tadpole and frog are quite different in
their apparent qualities, but we say that the resultant frog is
the same individual substance as the previous tadpole. If it
were a pet tadpole, called ' George ', the frog would be called
' George ' too (with one sole permissible exception, the change
to ' Georgina ' if it turned out to be a female). In the process
of transmutation George (or Georgina) has lost certain properties and been endowed with others. That is the natural
way of taking the process. If any further refinement of terminology is needed, these are provided for by the Aristotelian
' action ' and ' passion ', ' actualization ' and ' potentiality '.
The tadpole is potentially the frog and is in some sense trying
to be a frog. There is no *prima facie* reason why we should not
say the same about the water which turns to earth in Boyle's
experiment. So also for the Mercury which turns solid or
liquid or becomes *Sublimate, Mercurius Dulcis* or *Cinnaber*. Why
should not some of its properties change while others remain

unchanged, so that we still refer them to an ' it ' which remains identical, as we do with a growing animal or plant ? If ' it ' can change its properties while remaining the same ' it ', surely properties or qualities can be transferred from one ' it ' to another, as Berkeley supposed happened when you drank tar-water ? This was exactly what the alchemists said happened when you transmuted base metal into gold or silver. It is what the present day advocates of ' muck and mysticism ' in agriculture claim when they extol the virtues of compost and denounce the vices of ' chemicals '.

§4. The first step towards the new and not at all obvious chemical concept is not only to drop all analogies from the organic world, but also to drop all reference to the traditional four ' roots ' of things—Earth, Water, Air, Fire—at least in the traditional sense. It was unfortunate that the traditional ' roots ' had a certain survival value for physics (apart from chemistry) as suggesting four states of matter—Solid, Liquid, Gaseous, Incandescent (cf. the quotation from Newton). As suggesting what was simple and not composite they were a bit worse than useless, and worse still as including the old Ionian pairs of opposites—Hot and Cold, Moist and Dry. There was nothing to be said for them as ' elements ' ; they were *a priori* in the vicious sense ; they were of little help for any operation or technique for distinguishing between different kinds of objects or separating them. As Boyle pointed out nobody ever extracted earth, water, air or fire out of gold ; nor yet the mercury, sulphur or salt of later alchemy, unless these were first put in, Nothing has ever been extracted from gold except gold, so that there is no reason to suppose it to be composite in any way. Moreover its properties are found empirically to be highly specific ; density, melting point, hardness and other physical properties are always the same and different from those of any other metal or any body whatever. Gold, unlike other metals, is immune from attack by all chemical reagents (known in the 17th and 18th centuries), except *aqua regia*. In *aqua regia* it dissolves, and from the solution an orange crystalline substance can be obtained. When this is roasted the gold is recovered unchanged in properties and, with proper care, in quantity. When it is alloyed with other metals it can also be recovered again unchanged in quality and quantity. These properties are specific. Every specimen of gold, when carefully purified has them all, always. You cannot change one without changing all, as for instance by dissolving in *aqua regia*, and no other body that is not gold possesses any of them. The same can be said, *mutatis mutandis*, for silver and for some other metals. Thus gold has strong, definite claims to be considered a simple, single, enduring entity ; a species with unique specific properties. It is what Aristotle meant by *substance in the secondary sense*. (*Categories*, 2a. 14). It fulfills the requirements of an *infima species*. Until it was realised that there are chemical substances such as gold and silver, nobody was acquainted with anything like an *infima species*. The so-called *species* of the botanist and zoologist are all *genera*, capable of further subdivision into *sub-species, races, varieties*, in modern nomenclature. Gold and silver are not capable of such subdivision. All gold is (within certain specifiable limits) the same gold when it is sufficiently purified ; and the test for purification is that it shall be the same gold as before (i.e. no property is changed by further operations) or that it is indistinguishable from standard specimens accepted as pure. There is no vicious circle here, nor is it a matter of purely verbal or conventional definitions, because there is a technique, empirically discovered and applied for detecting and removing impurities. A substance is pure (within certain specifiable limits) when no further operations make any further difference. The qualification in brackets is an essential part of the definition of purity and of what constitutes a species ; it will be discussed later. In the meantime it may be well to insist that this part of the definition also is not purely verbal or conventional but is empirically based, as it must be if it is a primary definition (not secondary) in an empirical science.*

Granted that gold or silver is an *infima species*, or as near to one as we can expect to reach, is it more than that ? Are we

---

* The argument here put forward is the kind which Descartes could (and probably would) have put forward had he lived 150 years later, in place of his much weaker one about the wax (*Meditation* II).

justified in supposing that 'it' is a substance in more than Aristotle's secondary sense, that is in his primary sense? The evidence is that we can take a measured quantity of metal, put it through any process of transformation into compounds and alloys, and then recover it unchanged in quantity and character (within the limits of experimental error). What is more, we can, if we take sufficient trouble, follow 'it' as an 'historic route of occasions' (to use Whitehead's convenient terminology). In any one set of operations there is a specific, continuous, indeed unique, occupation of certain spatio-temporal volumes. A measured quantity of gold (and no other metal) is dissolved in *aqua regia* (and no other acid) and from that solution (and no other specimen) you recover a definite quantity of crystals of Chlor-auric Acid, the quantity depending on the quantity of gold originally dissolved (and no other kind of crystals). From them (and no other specimen) you recover your original amount of gold unchanged (and no other metal). It all happens within certain regions of space at certain times, nowhere else, and within those same regions only certain other compatible events are happening. Whether we can go on to speak of golden individuals as persisting, is another matter. That is how people tend to think of a gold ring or other cherished possession, but it leads to complications when we consider the metal before it was made into a ring, and again after it is melted down. The case is not quite the same as that of the tadpole and the frog, whose career begins and ends in a definite order. Clearly though, some kind of persisting 'it' has to be recognized, taken either more loosely as a *continuant* or more rigidly as a *substance* in the full Aristotelian sense.

The points to notice about the concept of chemical substance are : (1) it is a product of methods of separating and identifying and testing for purity; (2) it is the basis of classification and of all theory ; (3) it is an approximation, like other working concepts, yet it must stand for a *real* not just a *nominal* essence, in Locke's terminology. Let us take these points in order.

§5. The first step in the direction of chemical technique appears to have been the discovery of distillation. From quite early times people knew that if they boiled sea water in a cauldron and put a metal lid above it they could collect drops of potable water on the under side of the lid. It was a very crude kind of still ; it may have been used by seamen in distress, but nothing more came of it. Round about A.D. 100 or 200 the alchemists were using much superior methods. They were able to volatilize mercury and arsenic from ores of these elements in order to alter the surface colour of metallic surfaces ; and they did this in an apparatus that was quite an efficient still. Mary the Jewess who probably lived about that time in Alexandria is said to have described and very likely invented a quite well designed still.*

Distillation is a tricky process, seldom produces a pure product quickly and easily, even when its principles are understood ; but it is a process of separation or analysis, one of the two main types of separation available to the chemist. It consists of transfer through the vapour phase from liquid to liquid. It tends to concentrate the more volatile constituent, present in any mixture, in the receiving vessel at the beginning of the operation.

Sublimation, also known to the ancient alchemists, may be considered to be no other than a special case of distillation, or transfer through the vapour phase from solid to solid.

That is how the matter can be put now. It was a long time before the principles of distillation were understood, before there was even an inkling that it was a process of separation or analysis. Attention was mainly drawn to the mysterious efficacy of fire, and the mystery of the vapour state in which there is usually nothing visible. But the method was applied to all manner of things beside sulphides of mercury and arsenic ; and very rewarding the effort was in the way of potent brews ; hydrochloric acid, nitric acid (and when the two were mixed, the marvellous *aqua regia*), ammonia, a number of sulphur compounds, and by the middle ages alcohol or *aqua vitae*. All these provided enough to keep the alchemists busy and fairly

---

* See F. Sherwood Taylor, *The Alchemists*, 1951, pp. 37 *seq.* She is apparently one of the few authentic individuals mentioned in early alchemical writings. She is also credited with inventing that excellent device the water-bath, which the French, a chivalrous nation, still call after her, *bain-marie.*

happy even if none of their lead ever turned to gold. And of course they talked about the process in terms of transmutation and The Great Chain of Being.

The other process of separation available to the chemist is crystallization, transfer from liquid to solid phase. We may take precipitation as no more than a special case of crystallization, where the crystals form quickly and are therefore small. Under favourable conditions crystallization will produce, in one operation, a very nearly complete separation. It is the chemist's most powerful weapon. Again, the principles involved were not understood for a long time after it was used, nor was the process seen to be analytic. However, at some time and in some manner it was discovered by the alchemists. With its help, using the acids they obtained by distillation and by other means they prepared a number of salts in crystalline form. So began the process of providing the chemist with his enormous armoury of reagents.

One might add a third process, though it is analogous to crystallization, except that it is the liquid phase that is separated out, not the solid. This is the ancient process by which the noble metals are purified, which is still used for purposes of assay ; namely cupellation, heating the alloyed metal in an open crucible with an absorbent lining till all the base metal has oxidized and been absorbed in the lining.* It is specially important to notice that the principle of this process was not at first recognized. It was taken to be the creation or the resurrection from death of the nobler metal by the efficacy of fire. Take the practice, known in the ancient world, of recovering pure silver from the metal obtained by smelting silver-lead ores ; metal which looks just like lead. In the modern form of the process a blast of air is blown on the surface of the metal to drive the scum which forms to the side of the crucible where it is absorbed. At first the scum forms quickly so that the surface is dull. After a time it thins out, then there is a brief play of prismatic colours on the surface, and after that the gleam of pure silver. This was taken as the transformation of lead into silver. The creative (spiritual)

---

* At least as old as 1350 B.C. See J. R. Partington in *Science, Medicine and History, Essays for Charles Singer*, 1953, Vol I, pp. 35-46.

power of the fire, first of all is used to turn the ignoble ore into the nobler metal, but at the first treatment only into lead. Then in the cupellation it is again set to work to transform it into the still nobler form of silver, not, unhappily, into the noblest form of all. And why should the process not be seen that way? There is no reason at all, until the quantities concerned are weighed and the whole process more thoroughly examined. Then it will be found that the weight of silver recovered is very much less than the weight of metal put in, but that metallic lead can be obtained by heating the crucible lining with charcoal, and that if the operation is done carefully the combined weights of silver and lead at the end equal the weight of metal originally put in. There is no need to suppose that anything is radically transformed into anything else, only that pre-existing and surviving things are separated or combined. Mechanical, geometrical, mathematical categories suffice to give a useful account of the process, the silver and lead can be supposed to be there all the time, in the ore from the mine, in the mixed metal (as we now say) first obtained, in the scum on the surface of the cupel and in its lining, finally in the separated and purified metals which we can handle and examine at the end of the whole process. This is the useful account, vouched for by successful technique. The idea of transformation or transmutation adds nothing useful or technically valid. The question that remains to be asked is whether our account must be taken as complete because it is useful.

§6. Before the new point of view could be acquired it was necessary to use qualitative methods for identifying substances and for detecting impurities, and then from them to develop quantitative methods. That is the order ; there can be no quantitative methods before the others are established ; you cannot know how much you are doing before you have some idea of what you are doing.

The beginnings of qualitative analysis are prehistoric ; namely the tests for gold, the one thing people were really keen to identify and to obtain free of impurities. The first is the observation that gold does not tarnish in air, but that if it is heavily alloyed with metals other than silver (as we now express it), the resulting metal does tarnish. Then there is the touchstone test : gold rubbed on a polished black stone leaves a bright smear, the extent and colour of which varies with the amount of alloy. Brass and pyrites (Fool's Gold) give no streak on the stone. Heated in the furnace pure gold remains bright, and impure gold becomes purer on prolonged heating. Brass, which may look very like gold, completely loses its metallic character on prolonged heating in air. Albertus Magnus in the 13th century showed up the pretences of some contemporary alchemists in this way. A little more of his drastic inquisitiveness would have soon put a stop to such pretences. In later times there was the test with *aqua regia* which dissolves gold but not silver, while nitric acid dissolves silver but not gold ; a neat and characteristic example of qualitative method. There is also the density test for gold which was used by Archimedes and was a precise quantitative method, but apparently not used by anybody else.

Gold is the easy case ; silver not so easy ; other metals a bit more difficult ; non-metallic substances much more difficult.* Still, by the time of Agricola or Georg Bauer (*De Re Metallica*, 1556) sober and competent metallurgists had been at work and had produced the elements of quantitative methods of assay. The work of the alchemists is perhaps more important ; for they introduced laboratory methods and laboratory apparatus. This means essentially working on a small scale, quickly, accurately and of course cheaply ; and using special tools or apparatus designed for that special kind of work and scale of operations. This includes the special chemical reagents gradually produced, and by accident as often as by design. For the alchemists seldom knew what they were doing and their heads were full of speculations ; some philosophical though often very wild ; some commercial and downright dishonest.

Looking back in retrospect on the story, it is clear that no speculation is useful unless it is wedded to practice, to technique, and that practice must be guided by theory. Physics

---

* There are passages in Vitruvius which show some knowledge of how to test pigments for adulteration.

found the rudiments of both ready to hand and just went ahead with them. Chemistry could not find them, for they were not there (in spite of the Atomists). They had to be made out of nothing through centuries of fumbling.

§7. The child's first lesson in chemistry consists in learning the difference between (1) a chemical substance, elementary or compound, and (2) a mixture of substances, solution or metallic alloy. A substance, he is told, has fixed, specific properties. None can be altered without altering all, by chemical combination or decomposition to produce a new substance or substances. Mixtures (2) on the other hand have variable properties intermediate between those of the constituent substances. The constituent substances can be extracted from the mixture by suitable manipulation, by processes that are primarily physical rather than chemical, in the main by crystallization and distillation. What the poor child is not taught in his first lesson, but learns later by bitter experience, is that this distinction cannot be applied rigorously nor in all cases without the help of atomic theory ; though with that help (and certain qualifications) it can, and it forms the basis of chemical classification. In his first lesson the child is introduced to easy cases, where theory does not need to be conspicuously dragged in, and where he does not realise that theory is hovering in the background. Still, it is important that the distinction can be seen and empirically verified in some simple cases without theory. They suffice to show that theory is not purely conventional or the vicious kind of *a priori*. Confidence in theory then makes it possible to tackle the difficult cases, otherwise impossible.

Why is chalk considered to be one chemical substance and slaked lime to be another quite distinct one ? How can mixtures of the two, e.g. slaked lime after exposure to the atmosphere, be distinguished from the pure substances ? Chalk, which has been carefully prepared in a pure state or obtained naturally as crystalline calcite, contains 40% Calcium, 12% Carbon, 48% Oxygen, neither more nor less, within the limits of experimental error. Slaked lime carefully prepared in a pure state (not an easy thing to do) contains always 54·0%

Calcium, 43·3% Oxygen, 2·7% Hydrogen. Most specimens of slaked lime, however, will not be pure and will not have quite this composition ; they will contain some chalk or some quicklime or some water.

Q. How do you know they are not pure ?

A. Because they do not have the correct composition.

Q. How do you know that one composition is more correct than another ?

A. Because it is that possessed by the pure substance only.

Q. Is not this *petitio principii* ?

A. No ; it is saved by the atomic theory and by that alone.

Take another example ; the corresponding copper compounds, carbonate and hydroxide. It is difficult, if not impossible, to obtain anything having exactly the kind of composition that experience with calcium compounds would lead us to expect. Instead we find material of varying composition and with excess of water. Why then this dogmatism about the calcium compounds, if we cannot dogmatize about the copper compounds? The answer again is the atomic theory. As soon as we express composition in terms of atomic proportions and not percentages by weight the matter becomes clear, i.e. the proportions of the constituents of pure chalk or calcite give the formula $CaCO_3$ and those of pure slaked lime give the formula $Ca(OH)_2$; whereas nothing we get in the way of copper compounds is likely to give exactly or anywhere near $CuCO_3$ or $Cu(OH)_2$, but something in between. The naturally occurring crystals Malachite, $CuCO_3$. $Cu(OH)_2$ and Azurite, $2CuCO_3.Cu(OH)_2$, are the nearest thing. They are definite compounds but not pure carbonate or pure hydroxide. In the last resort the appeal is to the atomic theory.

If we stir up common salt with water, the salt disappears and the liquid obtained, though it retains some water-like properties and some salt-like ones, has some properties of its own that are different, e.g. it conducts electricity. We can in this way ' compound ' any quantity of salt we like, up to a certain maximum, with a given quantity of water. Traditionally, though, the result of this process is called a 'solution', a specially homogeneous kind of mixture, not a compound. Why? The answer is as before. Suppose it has been found that at some particular temperature (say 65°C.) the composition of a saturated solution of salt and water corresponded to $NaCl.5H_2O$, then there would be some suspicion that that solution at least might be a compound. If it were found also that the temperature of 65°C. and that composition defined a critical state for some significant physical property of the solution, say, density or viscosity, or better still both, then that suspicion would be well founded. We should take a solution of that composition at that temperature to be something more than just a mixture.

The constant boiling mixture of hydrochloric acid and water provides an interesting example. If a dilute solution of acid is distilled, the water boils off first until the remainder reaches a concentration of 20·24% acid, then it all boils over at constant temperature (110°C) and with constant composition. The same result is obtained by starting with more concentrated acid. The acid boils off first until the composition is 20·24%. The same thing would happen if there were a compound of hydrochloric acid and water. The composition 20·24% hydrochloric acid in water is very near to the atomic proportions $HCl.8H_2O$; is it a compound? The answer is, almost certainly not. A number of constant boiling mixtures are known, whose composition does not correspond to any simple atomic ratio. The composition of the hydrochloric acid and other mixtures is not quite constant but varies with the pressure, and therefore the temperature, at which distillation is carried out. Further, the existence of constant boiling mixtures can be predicted on thermo-dynamic grounds without appeal to the atomic or any kind of corpuscular theory.

Let us consider lastly an opposed example. The naturally occurring mineral oils consist (apart from traces of other elements) of carbon and hydrogen in varying proportions. They can be separated by distillation into fractions that are more volatile or less volatile, the more volatile contain rather more hydrogen, the less volatile contain rather less. The fractions are all readily soluble in one another ; they differ very little in physical and chemical characters, and such differences as there are grade imperceptibly into one another. Why do we not call them solutions of hydrogen and carbon, with perhaps a number of constant boiling mixtures ? The answer is that among the most volatile and easily distinguished fractions we do find substances of definite composition in definite simple atomic proportions and by analogy expect the rest to be similar. Using this analogy chemists entered on the excessively laborious enterprise of separating and identifying the compounds ; and so far have always succeeded. Given sufficient time and care definite compounds can be separated, and there is no sort of evidence for ' solutions ' of hydrogen and carbon. In short, faith in the atomic theory has enabled them to do, what mere empiricism could not have done.

§8. The atomic theory of the ancient Greeks must be reckoned as metaphysics, in their day and long after, and not yet as science. It was generic not specific. It rested upon arguments, mainly *a priori* as to what must really be true, whatever might be the appearances to the contrary ; and that surely is metaphysics, if anything is. It was not science, because up to the end of the 18th century no definite empirical conclusion was affected one way or the other by any hypotheses as to whether things are infinitely divisible or not. Corpuscular hypotheses were a luxury not a necessity of science ; the kind which Newton did not need to feign, and thought about only in his spare time.

While Newton was properly agnostic about hypotheses he was interested in their possibilities. He enunciated the fundamental thesis of the Kinetic Theory of Gases. By linking a corpuscular structure with the elastic properties of gases described by Boyle, he made the first approach to scientific use of theory of this type. The statement is :—' If a fluid be composed of particles fleeing from each other and the density be as the compression the centrifugal forces of the particles will be inversely proportional to the distances of their centres. Conversely, particles fleeing from each other with forces that are inversely proportional to the distances of their centres compose an elastic fluid whose density is as the compression '

[113]

(*Princ.* II, Prop. 23). Newton's formulation is misleading in introducing the idea of repulsive force instead of kinetic energy, but that was an error that could not be clearly seen till the 19th century. The theory was correctly formulated by D. Bernoulli in 1738.

Newton's statement lay fallow till, with the beginnings of quantitative chemical analysis of gases, Dalton made use of it to propound his atomic theory. Dalton's argument may be put in this form :—Suppose a compressible fluid, or gas, to be a pure elementary substance, then all the particles will be identical in all respects including their mass. Next suppose two such elementary gases capable of reacting to form a compound, say, hydrogen and oxygen, or hydrogen and chlorine. The combination can take place only if particles join up to form pairs, one from each gas ; or triads, one from one gas and two from the other ; or tetrads, one from one gas and three from the other or two from each ; or pentads ; or hexads, and so on. That is to say they will combine in fixed proportions by weight and there will be a *quantum* by weight in which each element combines in all its compounds, either a single one, or twice or three times, or some larger number, but still always a whole number. These numbers and the combining weights on which they are based can be discovered by the ordinary methods of quantitative analysis. This will be true, not only of gases but of liquids and solids, though the facts are made obvious by the properties of gases.

Dalton was not himself entirely clear about the business. He did not realise that the gas particles in an elementary gas were not necessarily the same as the combining *quanta* ; in short he did not make Avogadro's distinction between molecules, atoms and equivalent weights. Unfortunately, nature played a rather mean trick on him, by making the common elementary gases consist of molecules containing two atoms. Still, it might have been worse ; they might have contained five or six, and the atomic theory have waited another hundred years.

In this matter Dalton over-simplified, in another he failed to see how simple things really were. Gay-Lussac (1808) had put forward a Law of Combining Volumes of Gases, to the effect that gases combine in simple numerical proportions by volume. Thus it is found that two volumes of hydrogen combine with one volume of oxygen to give two volumes of steam (all reckoned at the same temperature and pressure). The law is a simple deduction from the Kinetic Theory of Gases, as now understood ; and gives the most direct and unequivocal method of determining atomic weights wherever it can be applied. Dalton, however, thought the simple ratios by volume were not at all exact, and those apparently established fortuitous. His own determinations of combining volumes of the oxides of nitrogen differed considerably from whole numbers, as did published figures of determinations by others. Gas analysis is a tricky business, as those who practise it know well even when provided with every modern convenience. When one sees the kind of apparatus that Dalton used, one is surprised that he got any results at all.

These errors and confusions were small matters. Dalton had provided an aim for the analysts, a criterion of accuracy and the rudiments of a notation, which the analysts, Berzelius and his followers, were quick to take up. In about a generation things were cleared up, and the basis of fact and theory established on which chemistry rests. Once you have decided that a substance is anything which is discovered empirically to have specific properties, not merely variable ones ; that a compound substance is one which can in fact be broken down into constituents and that elementary substances are those constituents which cannot in fact be broken down into simpler substances; once you have decided this, you have the rudiments of chemistry. Once you have decided that elements combine in definite proportions only, that where different proportions are possible they must vary discontinuously in the ratio of whole numbers, then you can tackle the difficult analytical problems already mentioned, and any others. The *a priori* and empirical are thus wedded, theory and practice are mutually dependent.

The ordinary plain man, for example the business man, revels in percentages and averages, which he takes as plain facts, but is deeply suspicious of chemical data presented in terms of atomic, molecular or equivalent weights, or, worse still, molar or normal concentrations of solutions. These all seem to him to be unintelligible, metaphysical and superfluous entities. The 19th century positivists, such as Ernst Mach and Wilhelm Ostwald, fought against the atomic theory along with the plain man. The positivist is a visualist (see Appendix) and he never condescends to handle anything except a type-writer. He cannot see atoms and therefore refuses to believe that working chemists do in fact handle them. When mixtures of hydrogen and oxygen of all sorts of composition are ignited, the result is always to produce triads containing 2 parts by weight of hydrogen and 16 of oxygen along with a residue of the pre-existing dyads of pure hydrogen or oxygen, whichever was in excess This is shown by means of further handling which is called analysis. That is to say, the processes of handling compel the small constituents of the large things handled to display properties belonging to discrete units of constant character. Had the 19th century chemists wavered in their faith in the atomic theory they would have failed in the difficult analytical work they accomplished so triumphantly; they would not even have attempted it.

The chemical atomic theory provides the key to all that can be done by chemical operations and to a classificatory system which can take care of the hundreds of inorganic substances and thousands of organic substances. It works as perfectly as any scientific theory has worked or is likely to work. No theory tells us all about everything and atomic theory has its limita-tions. Substance means pure substance, and no material ever handled is quite pure. Specific properties are never quite specific. All atoms of the same chemical element are not always exactly of the same weight (but the whole number rule can be applied to the variants). More awkward still in practice is the fact that criteria of identity and purity which apply perfectly to molecules of small size, say, up to those which contain a hundred atoms in the molecule, do not apply so well to molecules containing several thousands of atoms. Such molecules do exist and are not just oddities to be con-veniently ignored. The soluble proteins, which are among the most important constituents of the bodies of plants and animals, are instances. Let us take these points in order.

A question of the form, ' Is this a pure specimen of substance

A ? ', is answered *a priori* : ' No, because nothing is quite pure.'
The only positive and empirical answer is to say whether a
particular specimen contains less or more than a certain
amount of a certain impurity ; because if it contains more it is
useless for some special purpose for which that substance is
required. Most substances with any claim to purity are
artifacts and made for some special purpose. Naturally
occurring materials of any degree of purity are not very
common and have to be sought out and selected. Most of the
water on the earth consists of sea-water, which is not pure
enough for most human purposes, though pure enough for
marine animals. Most of the rest consists of ice and snow near
the poles or on the tops of mountains ; pure enough for many
purposes, but inaccessible. There are other smaller sources of
supply from which, by methods of selection, water can be
obtained that is pure enough for many purposes. Spring
water from certain mineralized regions contains small quantities
of lead salts in solution.* Such water is not pure enough for
drinking nor for use in an aquarium, but is quite pure enough
for boiler feed water. On the other hand water from streams
and lakes in mountainous country may contain enough
dissolved matter from peat to colour it conspicuously. Such
water is not pure enough for use in boilers, as the dissolved
matter is liable to corrode the water tubes, but it is quite pure
enough to drink, as the dissolved matter is harmless ; some go
so far as to say it is specially wholesome. Natural waters that
are pure enough for consumption by men, fish and boilers,
may still contain traces of calcium salts, chlorides, carbon
dioxide and oxygen. They will not be pure enough for many
laboratory and some industrial purposes and need further
purification. The same argument may be applied to any
substance used for any purpose ; gold that is pure enough for
making a ring is not pure enough for stopping teeth.

If we come down to considering, not parts per million
(10^{-6}) the more ordinary limit of significance in the way of
impurity, but parts per ten thousand million(10^{-10}) ; then
everything is impure and most chemical elements are to be

* 0.7 parts per million of lead are said to make water unsafe for human
consumption.

found in most solids or liquids. All food probably contains at least that amount of arsenic, but it does nobody any harm and nobody worries about it. Sea-water contains at least that amount of gold, and the total weight of gold contained in all the oceans must be very large. But it does no man, animal or plant any good or any harm, so far as we know. People have rather foolishly worried about it and companies have been floated to extract it. The companies, like the gold, have gone into liquidation without paying any dividends.

§9. This question of purity is one aspect of the larger question of specific properties ; the negative one. It is one of the specific properties of sugar that it does not have the poisonous properties of arsenic. Any specimen which is found to have such poisonous properties is said to be impure ; the properties are not attributed to the sugar, for that would be to deny that it was a substance or its properties specific. Specific, positive properties are not completely fixed and invariable, and the methods of determining them are all subject to error. Thus, though the density of sugar can be specified, and we can say quite definitely that anything which does not possess that density is not sugar, the specification is exact only within certain limits and it applies only under certain conditions (cf. Chapter V, Order in Nature). This causes no trouble as long as the limits are narrow enough for us to proceed as though all specimens coming up to specification were identical, or at least clearly distinguishable from all specimens of all different substances. That is pretty nearly true of substances with small molecules containing only a few atoms, up to, say, a hundred. It is quite untrue for large molecules. Yet it is possible, with some qualification, to apply to them the criteria of specific properties.

As an example of distinctions between small molecules take the case of the oxides of nitrogen.* There are five of these

* Observe the great convenience of the atomic notation for describing, naming and remembering. Very few could memorise the percentage compositions of the oxides of nitrogen, they have no obvious interrelations and in terms of them the names would have to be conventional and non-descriptive. As it is the names describe respectively the least oxygen content (-ous), the next (-ic), then numerically the number of atoms of oxygen. Nitrogen Peroxide is sometimes called the

differing according to the quantity of oxygen combined with the nitrogen, expressed in percentages for the sake of the plain man :—Nitrous Oxide (N_2O) has 36·4% of oxygen ; Nitric Oxide (NO), 53·4% ; Nitrogen Trioxide (N_2O_3), 63·2%, Nitrogen Peroxide (NO_2), 69·6% ; Nitrogen Pentoxide (N_2O_5), 74·1%. Even the crude methods of analysis used by Dalton enabled him to distinguish the first four of these substances (the ones known to him) because the steps between them, the minimum differences are large. They are large simply because the total number of atoms in the molecule is small. Contrast with them the proteins. They consist mainly of Carbon, Oxygen, Nitrogen and Hydrogen, some Sulphur, often a small amount of Phosphorus, and in special cases Iron, Zinc or other elements in small amounts. The smallest molecular weight recorded is about 17,000 (made up of more than a thousand Carbons (12), Oxygens (16) and Nitrogens (14) all linked together, and about a thousand Hydrogens (1) in between to fill up the spaces (leaving the few extras out of account). Two proteins, not of the most complex type, which have been very extensively studied may be taken as examples ; they are both readily soluble, can be obtained crystalline and are more easily purified than most. These are the Albumen of the Hen's Egg (Molecular Weight about 34,000) and the Hæmoglobin of the blood of man and others of the higher animals (Molecular Weight about 68,000). Hæmoglobin contains Iron and carries oxygen for respiration in virtue of forming a peculiar, reversible, chemical compound of oxygen. Notice that these molecular weights are twice and four times the minimum ; and many other proteins have molecule weights that tend round whole multiples of 17,000 ; though some have quite enormous molecular weights, running into millions. Clearly even in the smallest protein molecules three or four Carbons, Oxygens or Nitrogens more or less

Tetroxide and the gaseous molecule N_2O_4 does apparently exist, but so also does the half, NO_2, so it is somewhat anomalous. But on the whole the molecular composition is a guide to a useful nomenclature and for writing and for mnemonic purposes the molecular composition is most useful of all. For calculations and for describing chemical variations it is indispensable. Without the chemical equation, e.g. for the formation of water $2H_2 + O_2 = 2H_2O$, the reaction could not be described precisely.

would never be noticed, nor a few dozen Hydrogens. Quite considerable rearrangements within the molecule might go undetected too. Only broad differences are easily discernible ; minimum differences between one type of molecule and another are undetectable. It would be quite impossible to say whether all molecules were exactly alike, supposing by some chance they had been created so, and there is good reason to believe they were not created so. Methods of purification do not completely eliminate deviating units however strenuously applied. In fact excessive efforts at purification are very likely to alter the material and make it less homogeneous. Any account of the properties of a protein must be taken as a statistical average of a somewhat varying population. When the material is apparently homogeneous that means that most of the units in the population are very close to the average and only a few deviate much.

The most interesting point about the proteins is that they possess a uniform outline pattern which allows of endless variations in detail. They contain a backbone structure of long chains of Carbons, Oxygens and Nitrogens arranged in a certain order common to all proteins. The chains may be long or short, straight, coiled or twisted. Attached to the chains at the sides are a variety of molecular groups of different properties, some of which maintain cross linkages between chains. According to the arrangement of the chains and cross connections a protein may be threadlike and quite insoluble as hair or silk, or readily soluble, crystallizable, with globular and pretty regular molecules in solution, as egg albumen. Or it may possess molecular groupings attached to the chains which give it peculiar chemical properties, as hæmoglobin. In the body of any one animal there will be dozens, perhaps hundreds of proteins of different types performing different functions and throughout the animal kingdom very much the same general types are to be found. Within the mammalian group the protein types are very similar from one species to another. Nevertheless each species of animal has its own specific proteins, differing in minutiæ of atomic patterns within the molecule. For instance, the Albumen of the Hen's egg has been shown to differ from that of the Duck's egg. More important, each species has its own type of Hæmoglobin, differing slightly in the form of the crystals and in the way it reacts with oxygen to carry out its respiratory function. In effect, to cut a long story short, a man who had frog's hæmoglobin in his blood would have great difficulty in breathing, and a frog with human hæmoglobin would have as great difficulty. Each species has a hæmoglobin adapted to prevailing conditions of temperature, oxygen supply and blood constitution. Many small differences could be found within a single species of animal if anybody took the trouble to look for them. The different blood groups in man suggest this. These small differences may be partly due to differences in the average character of a protein population containing a variety of molecular types. If we represented possible closely related molecular types by the letters of the alphabet, then it would be as though one species of animal had some protein consisting mainly of type D, with a good many C and E, and a few B and F ; while a related species or race had it centring round F ; and that of more distantly related species centred round P, Q, or R.

The whole notion of a population and of average characters, indeed all other statistical notions, are derived from the study of human populations, and related studies connected with human affairs. Therefore it is worth having a glance at human statistics in order to bring out the resemblance and difference between them and small scale statistics of atom and molecule. There is one important difference. With human populations it is the individual who is seen and his characters observed—his height, age, income, length of life and so on. The population, the birth rate, death rate and other averages are inferred, theoretical entities. Men are seen to be born and die ; nobody has ever seen a birth rate or death rate, and no individual person has a birth rate or death rate. On the other hand, with atoms and molecules and other small scale entities it is not they but the population as a whole and the average that is seen and measured, the individuals are the inferred, theoretical entities. In the same way we see the shape of a sand dune and from the steepness of the slope on the leeward side, can infer something about the (very different) shapes of the sand grains.

We say (assuming it to be true for sake of illustration) that the Patagonians are the tallest men and the Siamese the shortest. That does not mean that every Patagonian is taller than every Swiss or Egyptian, and every Siamese shorter. It does not even mean that every Patagonian is taller than every Siamese. It does mean that in the Patagonian population tall men over 6 ft are numerous, in the Siamese very rare ; and at the other end of the scale the other way about. It also means that all precise statements about heights of Patagonians or Siamese are statements about averages of various kinds obtained by statistical computations of some kind, simple or elaborate. It also means that all such statements are about what happens for the most part, not about what must happen in every or in each individual case. In fact they are not statements about individuals at all. Lastly it means that the larger the population or group the more reliable the statement. Statistical assertions about populations of a dozen units or individuals are not to be relied on, assertions about populations of millions of millions may be extremely reliable. On the whole the great reliability and precision of generalizations in physics is the result of their being statistical generalizations about very large populations. That a law is statistical does not make it less of a law. It does mean though that for reliability and precision, not only must the population be very large, but also very homogeneous or else, if heterogeneous, stably distributed and at random (cf. Chapter IX, §1 below). This is where the difficulties begin in the biological realm, where there is variety, instability and non-random distribution. In touching on the properties of proteins we have crossed over from the purely chemical to the partly biological. The purely chemical realm is, in the first instance, a realm of artifacts, and if chemistry and experimental physics are called natural science, ' natural ' is a courtesy title.

§10. Though the concept of specific properties could be deduced from the atomic theory in its ancient form, and though Archimedes possessed the concept, it had to win its way into modern science independently and began to do so in the 18th century. When Dalton's atomic theory had been cleared of confusions by Cannizaro in the mid-19th century one would suppose the battle had been won. Even so positivists and phenomenalists struggled right up to the end of the century to get rid of the atomic theory, though it meant picturing a world of loose transferable adjectives, after the manner of alchemy and not of chemistry. Twentieth century Quantum Theory is based on the study of atomic spectra, the last refinement of measurement of specific properties. The concept of specific properties is also needed for the treatment of organic form, as that is discovered by the biological sciences.

So much for the importance of the notion ; next as to its peculiar character. Like other basic concepts it is technical, it depends upon what we do to and with things. It also depends upon what we cannot do, unlike the older physical concepts, but like a number of the more important newer ones, those which Sir Edmund Whittaker has called Postulates of Impotence (cf. Chapter X, §3). Examples of these in physics are, The Three Laws of Thermodynamics, The Principle of Relativity, The Uncertainty Principle. Let us award ours the dignity of a Principle and state that there are properties of things we can by no means separate and can alter at all only under certain conditions and within certain limits. In short, substances have constant natures which just have to be discovered. For all that, the constant natures or substances of chemistry are artifacts to the extent that they have to be artificially isolated before they can be examined, and the mode of isolation is part of their specific properties. From this it comes about that we can take a substance as an Aristotelian species and as having an ' essence ' revealed in the processes of manipulating it.

What has been said above about the proteins and what is to come in the next chapter about organic forms should help to indicate an important connection between chemical and biological concepts. This connection must not be permitted to obscure the differences. Living organisms are not artifacts of any kind ; they are just *found* and not *made*. Whatever may be their ' natures ' or ' essences ' these are not open to inspection and are not necessarily constant. The concepts of biology are still technical, but the technique is not that of the artisan

I [123]

but of the cultivator, herdsman and physician, who combine between them the apparently beneficent technique of nurture and the less beneficent technique of slaughter.

One last comment needs to be made before leaving the subject of chemistry. Its fundamental concept of substances with specific properties is distinct from any of the fundamental, geometrical, arithmetical or mechanical concepts of classical physics and any of its spatio-temporal transactions. The concept arose in a different way, and has certain definite consequences which are clearly seen in biology and nowhere else.

All atoms of the same isotope of the same element are held to be identical ; not closely similar, but identical in all respects (*pace* Leibniz). The differences between different isotopes of one element are chemically negligible and among most of the elements of biological importance the vast bulk of the material is of one isotope. As a result the atoms composing the bodies of organisms are perfect units (bricks) for building complex regular structures and all the constituent molecules of living cells. Nearly all molecules of water are composed of Hydrogen (1) and Oxygen (16) and are the same in all respects. Very occasionally a molecule of heavy water will come along, but chemically it is the same and it does not interfere. So with the other simple molecules that are the tools of the organism. There are hundreds of chemically possible sugars and sugarlike substances. Living organisms construct only a few of them and for the most part they use one, d-glucose, in preference to all others. Again, every molecule of ordinary d-glucose is the same as every other. Organisms have at their disposal these ' working parts ' of identical character, which work with precision however many of them are in use. On the other hand the structural components, the very large molecules, though built on a uniform ground plan with a limited number of kinds of identical ' bricks ' are capable of endless variation by different arrangement in detail of these ' bricks '. Here is, in part, the explanation of the combination of order with variety that is displayed by living things and is the basis of individuality and choice. These are notions entirely alien to classical physics, but not to a chemistry which includes the chemical structure of living organisms.

CHAPTER VIII

ORDER IN THE ORGANIC WORLD

No simple biological picture · The concept of organic forms · Cell theory and other basic theories · Digression on evolution and genetics · Organic form again · Taxonomy · Statistics and populations · Behaviour of organisms

§1. To save repetition I would ask the reader to keep in mind the analogy between chemistry and biology which was drawn at the beginning of the previous chapter. It may be difficult to bear in mind because nowadays chemistry is seldom thought about as an autonomous discipline, but taken to be a subordinate and dull branch of physics. It is true that in the last fifty years chemistry and physics have become far more closely linked, and this could be taken as meaning that physics has swallowed chemistry. But swallowing is quite the wrong metaphor. It has been more like a marriage, and the new science of atomic structure and quantum physics is the offspring of the older sciences. It should be called chemico-physics or physico-chemistry.

It is easy enough to give a general account of chemistry because its methods and basic concepts are clearly its own and nobody else's and are compact and homogeneous. There is no such ease about biology. For many purposes it is convenient to distinguish a number of different biological sciences ; indeed it is commonly done and over-done till the multiplication of names and supposed disciplines has become inconvenient. After all, living organisms do have this character in common, that they are alive ; and it is the most striking thing about them, at least for those who look at them while they are alive and not only after they have been pickled and become artifacts.* This common character can be correlated with a common chemical ground plan of structure and function, in spite of all diversity of form and behaviour. We can say that without a structure of nucleic acid, protein, carbohydrate, fat

---

* ' Thus, to a really learned man, matter exists in test tubes, animals in cages, art in museums, religion in churches, knowledge in libraries.' A. N. Whitehead, *Essays in Science and Philosophy*, 1947, *Harvard : the Future.*

(as a minimum list) and without certain basic types of chemical change among them there is no life. But we find also, and here the difficulties begin, bewildering variety and complexity of form and behaviour. For the ordinary 20th century man the organic world consists of a few domestic animals and garden plants with a vaguely conceived background of pests and nuisances, and he does not realise the variety of it all. Nor do a great many narrowly trained specialists who claim to be biologists, e.g. those who take the animal kingdom to consist exclusively of the banana fly (*Drosophila melanogaster*).

Because of this variety and complexity a general survey of biological science or sciences, a general statement of methods, concepts and basic theory does not take us far. We have to say that biology is whatever biologists do and then have to confess that they do many different apparently unrelated things, because they find that different groups of organisms behave in different ways. Theory if it is to apply generally fades off into vague truisms. In any case biological theory of the basic type (not loose speculation, of which there has always been too much) is humdrum with none of the excitements of theoretical physics. Compact classical researches suitable for the case history method of exposition are few.

Pasteur's work in destroying the superstition of spontaneous generation is classical, its practical outcome positive, but its theoretical outcome negative for all its importance. Much biological theory is of this kind. Unlike physics, biology does not turn 'postulates of impotence' into positive concepts (cf. Chapter X, §3).

As the biologist deals with what he finds and not with artifacts which he makes one might suppose that he would find his theory by way of pure contemplation of Platonic forms. That is not how it has turned out. Rather, the biologist's theory is tied up with what he does, with his technique. It has its roots in agriculture and medicine. Theory tends to be prescriptive—' Handle this organism in this way for preserving or destroying, not in that because . . . '

§2. Let us begin at the beginning. Farmers, hunters, fishermen and housewives have from time immemorial identified with very fair precision a number of species of animal, tame, wild, useful and harmful ; also a number of species of plants, edible, medicinal, poisonous and, less precisely, a number of weeds. The total number of familiar species in any one part of the world runs to hundreds, and taking the whole of the world together probably to thousands. Sound methods of identification are there but no systematic classification ; even Aristotle lumped together crabs and clams, as ' shell-fish ', after the popular fashion. A good deal of simple anatomy and physiology is there too ; information as to what animals eat (and how they should be eaten), where they live, how they breed, how fast they grow, and so on. There is also some corresponding information about plants, but less of it and less reliable. To men, who are not plants, their life is more mysterious than that of the higher, larger and more familiar animals. All this folklore is rudimentary biology, most of it sound enough, though with a sprinkling of old wives' tales (cf. Chapter II, §4, Aristotle on Teeth). I venture to suggest that this biological folklore, available to every country dweller throughout human history, constitutes a larger body of more reliable and useful information than is now possessed by the ordinary town-dweller of any level of education. He derives his information from print, which is bad, or the cinema, which is worse, or other ' media of mass communication ' as they are appropriately called. He never checks anything by his own observation ; he does not want to and could not, if he did want to. But this rural folklore was loose information, it was not coordinated, it had no coherent theory belonging to it ; it was not science in the full sense.

If we follow up the clue which I hope is to be found in the previous chapters, we shall look for the beginnings of genuine science in the practice, the technique of the pre-scientific stage. Now, successful identification of an individual animal or plant as belonging to a species is the beginning of successful technique : to distinguish wheat from barley and both from tares, to distinguish sheep from goats and both from wolves, to distinguish young from adult, male from female, healthy from diseased. Identification depends upon *precise* appreciation of *organic form* * throughout a life history, and of the inter-relation of different types with one another, and with the environment. (No biology without ecology.) The adjective ' precise ' is the operative word, because without the microscope to reveal minute structure, naked-eye observation does not go far enough, and can be positively misleading. For this reason the history of biology hardly needs to begin before the 17th century—with all respect to the admirable efforts of the earlier pioneers. For one thing, and one only, we must go further back. It is impossible to doubt that Dr. C. E. Raven (Gifford Lectures, Vol. I, *Science and Religion*, 1953, pp. 58 *seq.*) is right in maintaining that in Western Europe, the artists were the first to observe and record natural forms with *precision*. The word here has another special meaning that takes us beyond microscopic technique or anything analogous to the exact metrical methods of the physical sciences. It means also loving interest in the artistic perfection of organic form, a perfection found equally in large outlines and minute detail. Without that interest a man may be an applied physicist, a plant or animal engineer, but not a biologist in the complete sense, and not a morphologist at all.

This has to be very strongly emphasized because there is a widespread belief that biology is just plant and animal engi-neering and that ' natural history ' is a childish game, rather like collecting match-box labels, or else a tiresome preliminary which can be done by some menial, not the real and interesting business. This is the view of would-be technocrats who despise everything they cannot control, or of short-sighted laboratory technicians who see nothing outside the laboratory. Of course, plant and animal engineering has its place. A great deal of bacteriology is just that—' a low form of gardening '.

§3. When the study of organic form extended down to the microscopic structural unit, the cell, then and not before,

* See A. Arber, *Natural Philosophy of Plant-Form*, 1950 ; especially pp. 1-8 on plant form as the analogue of animal behaviour and pp. 162 *seq.* on Cause and Sequence.

See also her later book, *The Mind and the Eye*, 1954, especially her useful re-minder of the saying of von Sachs : ' Was man nicht gezeichnet hat, hat man nicht gesehen.'

organic theory could begin. Without a microscope, and a pretty good one, the biologist has only half an eye. Let me try to summarize the elementary biological theory that has ensued from the full use of both eyes, and the hands also. It comes conveniently under three heads.

(i) All living organisms consist of cells : single separate cells, ordered aggregates, or, occasionally, *syncytia*, fused masses of initially separate cells. The order of the ordered aggregates may be rudimentary, as in the strings of cells produced by repeated division of simple algae, or a highly organized and integrated structure, as among the higher animals. At all stages each cell (or *syncytium* such as the separate ' fibres ' of the muscles of higher animals appear to consist of) is itself a living organism, has a certain minimum complexity of structure and function, is a unit or ' atom ', or perhaps it would be better to say in Newton's terminology, a ' corpuscle '. This is the justly famous cell theory, arrived at independently by the botanist M. J. Schleiden (1804-81) and the zoologist T. Schwann (1810-82), and first published by the latter in 1839.

The generalization applies to all green plants, namely those which utilize the energy of sunlight to synthesize their tissues from inorganic compounds, and to all animals which live by eating plants, at first hand or at second hand by eating other animals or by living as parasites upon them. It applies also to the more complex among the saprophytic plants (e.g. fungi and moulds) which have no green pigment but absorb already synthesized organic material. It applies partially to most bacteria which are reckoned as unicellular saprophytic plants, but appear to lack the full complexity of structure and function of the plants proper. It hardly applies to the ' viruses ' which seem to be partly living, more like cell fragments than cells and entirely parasitic on living cells. To be on the safe side let us ignore residual or eccentric forms (though many and interesting), and consider ordinary plants and animals about which there is less doubt, particularly as to when they are alive or dead.

(ii) Granted (i) we can describe the process of multiplication or growth by cell division and the process of sexual reproduction. However complex and however different their life history all organisms begin it as single cells. But owing to these complexities and divergencies nothing more can be said in general terms. The life history of each species has to be worked out for that species. Gross blunders have been committed by forgetting that ; for instance in attempts at malaria control directed against the wrong species of mosquito. If examples need to be multiplied, consider the vagaries of sexual and asexual reproduction, and of parasitism and symbiosis. Or consider a more familiar one, and that within a species, the vagaries of ' exogamy ' in apple varieties so that one variety is fertilized only by pollen from certain other varieties.

Characteristically, biological theory, as opposed to physical, has to be stated extremely vaguely, and general theory says very little about any one specific case. Even the more specific generalizations suffer the same defect. It is this which disposes of the dreams of so many learned men, of biological theory set out in algebraical equations like physical theory, and applicable all round to any problem that crops up. Would any one really want a comprehensive formula if it meant solving a hundred simultaneous equations with a hundred variables in each ? Even if the mathematical manipulations were easy, think of the problem of finding the values of the constants, correct to fifty or a hundred or two hundred figures or thereabouts. The dream is too much like a nightmare.

(iii) It is a relief to turn to the plain good sense of the theory of *biogenesis*. This is that *every living organism is the descendant of similar organisms*, organisms of the same species. At the present day (whatever may have happened in the distant past when the earth was new and its surface and atmosphere quite unlike those we know, the product of millions of years of organic activity) lifeless material does not give rise to living organisms of any sort high or low, vegetable or animal. It does not even produce viruses ; in fact, these least of all. If this generalization were seriously at fault then the industries of food preserving, fermentation and many others would be thrown into confusion and bankruptcy, as would the practice of medicine and surgery.

This generalization (iii) is a corollary of the cell theory, but was established with difficulty against strenuous, indeed violent opposition from the supporters of *abiogenesis*, the view that lifeless matter can and does by itself give rise to living organisms by ' spontaneous generation '.* It needs to be stated in terms that allow for some variation of form from one generation to another and of considerable variation in the course of many generations. The child is very like its parents in many ways but not quite in all. It may be in many ways quite unlike any of its ancestors 100,000 generations ago.

§4. Here a digression is needed to say a word about subjects that are not so fundamental but loom large in the public mind and the minds of some biologists, who really ought to know better. In the course of many generations organisms have changed in the past and presumably are changing still. The fauna and flora of the most ancient fossil-bearing rocks are not the same species as the fauna and flora now living, although there are some very ancient types still surviving comfortably in the sea, an environment which changes little and very slowly. Even in the sea the predominant forms are relatively modern. This is plain matter of fact, a plain empirical generalization as well authenticated as any. So far as this is the doctrine of evolution there is nothing exciting or difficult or doubtful about it, not at least in a general way. But when it comes down to details, as to the history of any special group of forms there are difficulties because the evidence is fragmentary.† When it comes to deciding what has caused changes to come about in any special case then there are immense

* Pasteur won the battle for biogenesis in the 1850's with help from Tyndall, who approached the subject from an entirely different point of view. But he had practically no other help. In the earlier 19th century belief in abiogenesis was universal as it had been in the time of Virgil. This was in the face of contrary arguments adduced by Redi (1621-97), John Ray (1627-1705), Leeuwenhoek (1632-1723), Spallanzani (1729-99) and Schwann (1810-82). A strange case of old wives' tales prevailing over observation and good sense, and of unscientific behaviour by the majority of scientific men.

† Notice how cautious botanists (who are not themselves plants) are about the course of plant evolution compared with the cocksure zoologists who know it all leads up to their own noble selves.

difficulties and proposed answers to questions are highly speculative.

On the general question, once anybody has grasped the immensity of the time scale involved, a time scale of thousands and millions of generations, there is no difficulty. Had it been explained to Aristotle he would have raised no objections. His doctrine of fixity of species was based on a very short time scale, a commonsense one of a few generations. St. Augustine would almost certainly have raised no objection either. The ancient world had no bias in favour of a short time scale with strictly defined limits, such as grew up later. St. Augustine understood the process of Creation as a long-lasting continuous process. St. Thomas Aquinas might have hesitated a bit more because of that later tendency. But I believe the trouble began later and mainly with bibliolatrous, materially-minded Protestants who took to interpreting the Old Testament in legalistic and mechanistic terms, and cared nothing for the Prophets. It was these people who asserted, what nobody had taken seriously or perhaps even thought of before, that the world was created in the year 4004 B.C. in six days of twenty-four hours each by the clock. This is one of the most striking examples of misuse of the categories of physical science, and would have puzzled and amused ancient Hebrew scribes.

Granted that there have been changes in organic forms, the question whether these were changes for the better or the worse in some moral sense is the one which has caused the excitement. It is not a question the biologist is called upon to answer and it may be intrinsically meaningless. It appears to have a meaning because we can ask whether the changes were for better or worse in an æsthetic sense and we can attribute cosmic or theological significance to such æsthetic judgments ; rightly or wrongly, certainly rashly.

Undoubtedly biologists can point to one factor which must have operated to produce organic change ; Darwin's ' natural selection '. This means that forms which are less suited to any environment in which they find themselves tend to die out in favour of those better suited. It does not however explain how they come to find themselves in that environment nor how the changes in their forms have come about. It is customary to say that changes come about by *chance* ; legitimately, if to say so amounts to a confession of ignorance. Thus the doctrine of natural selection is negative. It is the biological equivalent of the 2nd Law of Thermodynamics ; it states that types, like individuals tend to die out. Whatever the rate of dying out may be it always holds. If forms change, if forms remain unchanged, if some organisms die out, if others survive, natural selection explains it all equally easily. Thus it can be used as a blanket to smother further questions. This is not to say that it does not have a legitimate use ; only, that its exponents frequently use it otherwise.*

Granted that organic forms change in course of time, in the long run, though in the short run populations are generally stable ; the question then arises : What makes them change ? What are the causes of variation ? It is an awkward question and it was wise of Darwin to leave it deliberately unanswered (quite in the Newtonian tradition : *Hypotheses non fingo*). It is also a paradoxical question. Causes are discovered by observing regularities and in the physical sciences irregularities are dismissed as ' errors ' or simply ignored. Our evolutionary question about a long term process of variation on the statistical scale affecting whole populations we should make our second one, because such variation is derived from primary or short term variations among individuals composing the population. However, it is convenient to take this secondary question first as it can be dealt with quickly, and the other one is the important one.

All our actual information about variation is based on observation of relatively short term processes, on what happens in the course of a few years (in accurate carefully controlled observations) or in the course of a few hundred years (in less controlled looser observations). But we want to know what happens in several thousand years and in several million years. Moreover, most of our information is based on domestic plants and animals (e.g. *Drosophila melanogaster*), which may not be fair samples. It is rash to argue from them to undomesticated

* Those who claim that *everything* comes about by chance and natural selection are perhaps sufficiently refuted by the retort that the noises they make have no significance because they are the result of chance and *natural* selection, not the utterer's selection.

organisms, including man himself, only doubtfully domesti-
cated.

Lamarckians have claimed from time to time to show
direct influences from the environment producing a change in
the genetic make up of a race of organisms in a few generations.
So far all such claims made for the higher plants and animals
have been bogus.* Indeed Lamarckian claims based on a few
generations are generally unplausible. If populations or even
small numbers of individuals could change their genetic
constitution as quickly as all that populations would not be as
stable as they obviously are. Either evolution would be a very
rapid business or it would be quite impossible because populations would not have sufficiently stable or definite characters
to be subject to natural selection.

The Mendelian geneticists oppose the Lamarckian claims
and say, in elaborate technical terminology, that variation is
due to *chance*, and evolution is the result of ' natural selection '
of favourable *chance* variations. If, when they say ' chance ',
they mean simply that *they do not know what causes* variations
to occur, then their position is secure, in fact impregnable.
If they mean by ' chance ' that *they know that there are no causes*
of certain sorts at work, then their claims are no better than
the Lamarckian. They have no evidence that Lamarckian
inheritance may not occur over long periods of time. Nor
have they any evidence that there is no kind of directive long
term process, a Bergsonian *élan vital*, at work. Surely, on
this whole question of how evolution works, in what direction
if any, the truly scientific attitude is strictly agnostic. Speculative convictions on one side or the other range from
dogmatic metaphysics, at the best, to superstition at the
worst, though most of it is about the middle range of ' science
fiction '.

Leaving out of account speculations about what has
happened in the distant past as the result of which things now
are as they are, let us concentrate on the present or near past,

---

* The case of the unicellular organisms is at present *sub judice*. However
Lamarckian they might turn out to be that will not prove that the higher organisms
are equally Lamarckian and non-Mendelian. And the evolutionary problem
is about the higher forms ; nobody is yet in a position to discuss the evolution of
the rest. See also H. Graham Cannon, *The Evolution of Living Things*, 1958.

on what can now be seen and is beyond reasonable doubt. There are three conspicuous marks characteristic of living organisms. There is (1) the relatively uniform chemical ground plan, mentioned already ; a ground plan that admits of indefinite elaboration and variation. Then (2) there is the immensely lavish way in which elaboration and variation of form has actually occurred. The imagination boggles at it, and the more anybody examines the variety of living forms the bigger the boggle. It is a variety of *types*, each type stands for an order of its own distinct from other orders and yet related to them. It is a cosmos with very little chaos, as the lifeless world is not. But also (3) within any type form there is room for individual variation. These variations are as significant as the uniformities. They cannot be ignored or dismissed without falling into serious error. Obviously, however, we must take regularity first.

§5. Organic form is geometrical, but as it is growing, changing, responding to mechanical stresses it must be taken mechanically, as, at least, four dimensional geometry of space-time. To take it purely visually, or in two dimensions, or as any algebraical equivalent, however ingenious, will reveal nothing or even deceive. Let me suggest a very few general examples. Why are the larger and smaller land living animals never of the same external geometrical form, even when basic structural and chemical schemes are closely similar ? Consider the mammals from largest to smallest, or, on a narrower range, the birds ? And why, again, is the bird range narrower at the upper end not the lower ? It is because they all have to cope with a permanent gravitational field, which bears more hardly on them the bigger they are, An elephant built on the model of a mouse, or worse still a jerboa (desert rat), would not be able to stand or walk. A mouse built on the model of an elephant could stand but could do nothing else. This is a question of what must be of necessity, not of probability. The same argument applies to the flight of birds and of insects too. In complete contrast, marine animals can be of almost any shape at almost any size, because they have no gravitational field to bother about. Only death by misadventure stops marine animals growing, whereas land animals definitely stop growing at a certain size and age. Fishes of the same normal streamline form (e.g. trout or herring, not eel or flounder) can be any length from less than 1 cm. to 10 m. or more. The whales, with a different internal structure, have much the same external form and grow bigger still. For these and many other similar points see D'Arcy Thompson, *Growth and Form*, 1948.

The radial symmetry in a horizontal plane of the larger land plants is the result of coping statically rather than dynamically with the gravitational field. Marine plants have no such symmetry. Also plant growth, because tied down to one spot, is labile according to the external conditions at that spot. Consider for example, four common kinds of tree, Oak, Ash, Spruce, Scots Fir, as seen growing under different conditions : (i) growing freely with plenty of room, sun, soil and water, and in shelter, each developing its own characteristic form unchecked : (ii) growing excessively lean and high, crowded together : (iii) growing in an exposed place on poor soil, stunted and bowed by the wind. Each kind still retains its own characteristic form and yet is changed by the different conditions in the same kind of direction. The general plan of the growth process and the effect of conditions can be portrayed in outline by an artist with a few pencil strokes, even if the details are too much for him. He can do it because his drawing is itself a dynamic process to be interpreted dynamically. The process can also be discussed abstractly in Aristotelian terms (see Appendix).

Biological theory cannot do without geometry, mechanics, physics and chemistry. It needs all it can get and has often been held up for lack of them—of the right sort ; there may have been plenty of other sorts available. The right sort consists of specific methods and specific theories for dealing with specific problems. They all have to be found empirically and have to be applied *ad hoc*.

The basic contribution that needs special emphasis comes from chemistry ; not general chemistry but chemistry of a peculiar sort already referred to in Chapter VII, §9. It is important because the small scale basis of order in organic form is a chemical ordering process embodied in proteins and other large molecular structures, that build up the visible structure of the living cell. That is the basis of the order ; the disorder is also important. It is the disorder of aqueous solutions, which allow of change of shape and position and allow of order being broken up and then reconstituted as before ; or else not quite as before, but in a new order. In short, there is order without rigid determination and freedom without chaos.*

Lastly, as to the individual cell. It is autonomous, up to a point and within limits, but in the higher organisms is a constituent of a larger whole to which it is subordinate and which regulates its behaviour. This macroorganism is also a unit, an individual ; not less so than the cell, but more so at the top of the animal scale. In saying this I am stating part of what is meant by saying that the macroorganism can also be a conscious agent.

Far below the level at which we can detect conscious agency, organic activities have *direction* or if you prefer, *purpose*, though it is a risky term to use. Perhaps the best term is *function*, which can be used in the widest sense (cf. A. A. Bowman, *A Sacramental Universe*, 1939). and is equally applicable at all levels from virus to man. In terms of function and of structure subserving function we can speak of *normal* and *abnormal*. Normality need have nothing to do with averages. If 99% of the population were blind or mad and only 1% could see or were sane, the blind or mad would still be abnormal because less effective or with impaired function. We could however say that such a population taken collectively was abnormal, because of the very small ratio of effectives to ineffectives. But function and effectiveness are the test of normality, not numbers.

Consider only the minimum functions of growth, nutrition

---

* Cf. R. S. Lillie, *General Biology and Philosophy of Organism*, 1945 (University of Chicago Press). The mycetozoon *Badhamia utricularis* in its plasmodium or fluid, amœboid stage is a vast syncytium which creeps forward over the fungus it eats (e.g. *Stereum hirsutum*). It has a characteristic but labile large-scale, naked-eye form (see diagrams in textbooks) but very little form to be seen under the microscope. It can flow through blotting paper and then reconstitute its characteristic form on the other side.

and reproduction, they require the notions of health and disease, good adaptation and bad, normality and abnormality. None of these conceptions have any applications to or any meaning for a lifeless world. (They apply to human artifacts, which are themselves lifeless but would not exist in a lifeless world.) In a crystal of radium salt about 41 radium atoms out of every 100,000 explode every year. Are those that explode abnormal or unhealthy, or eliminated by natural selection ? Is it normal for a stone to roll down a hillside, or to stay where it is ; for a river to change its course or stay as it is ; for the tide to be high or low ; for the sea to remain salt or the moon cold or the sun hot ?

One basic difference between any living organism and any lifeless thing is that the organism is self-centred (cf. Spinoza on *conatus*, *Ethics*, Pt. III, Pro. 7), while the other has no self and no centre, except accidentally in a purely geometrical sense. The organism, having a self and centre takes in what it *needs* from the environment, gets rid of what it does not *need* and even moulds the environment to its *needs*. (I have italicized *needs* to indicate that anybody who objects to teleological terms can find others for himself.) The green plant builds up its own substance from carbon dioxide, water and dissolved salts, and arranges the material according to its own specific pattern (cf. remarks about the growth of trees above). Animals go further than that. The caddis-worm builds a little tunnel in which to hide ; the stickleback builds a nest within which he persuades his wives to lay eggs and guards the eggs against hungry prowlers (including the wives) ; the bird builds her nest (with or without male assistance), broods on her eggs and feeds the young till they can fend for themselves. There is no need to go on to mention human technological efforts. In all cases we can distinguish between efforts that are usually successful or well adapted and those that are usually unsuccessful or ill adapted. In some cases also we can distinguish behaviour which is adapt*ed* to a particular environment which provides a specific stimulus, but not to any other, from behaviour which is also adapt*able* and can respond successfully to different environments. Adaptable behaviour is more conspicuous at the higher levels of organic life, but it is very rash to deny its existence at any level (cf. again the growth of trees mentioned above).*

When we speak of an individual organism being self-centred it is obvious that besides the individual and its own self there is something else which is not so visible or definable and may not have a self or a centre or be an organism. We may call this the species or race or society or use some other collective noun. At any rate the bird and the stickleback build their nests *for* the eggs, not *for* themselves. Even the caddis-worm is not so completely self-centred as he looks at first sight ; though undeniably he is self-centred, as are bird and stickleback.

Nothing that has been said above means that living organisms are exempt from the laws of physics as they apply to lifeless things. Rather, it is the opposite, that the laws of lifeless things are merely statistical laws of how things happen to shake down together when they are left to themselves. (R. O. Kapp, *Science versus Materialism*, 1940.) Living things on the other hand have their own order and are subject to the laws of that order which has to be maintained against the tendency of all physical aggregates to become more and more chaotic. The difficulty is that ' chaos ', ' disorder ', ' randomness ', ' chance ' are not names for kinds of things we discover in the world, but refer to our failure to discover, or decision to ignore or to treat as irrelevant. The distribution of players on a cricket field is random for the spectator who has never heard of cricket, or for the doctor who is interested only in their diseases or the tax-collector who is interested only in their incomes. Everything in our experience is partly orderly and partly disorderly ; the distinction comes of our selection in accordance with our interests. Moreover complete order or complete disorder is unimaginable.

§6. We must now return to the starting point, the grouping and classifying of organic forms, or, in one word, to taxonomy. Of late the problems of taxonomy have been neglected by the

* A machine, however complex, is always adap*ted*, never adap*table*. It responds in a predetermined way to a number of pre-selected types of situation. If a machine ever does anything else it is said to have broken down and is over-hauled and repaired or else scrapped. The needs to which it is adapted are those of the designer, maker, and user ; the machine has none.

wise and prudent, or those who consider themselves to be such. As a result much laboratory work is done by people who do not know one species from another and much of whose work is therefore wasted. Taxonomy is still necessary, still difficult and still interesting ; so it is a pity it should be neglected. The main difficulty, to put it briefly, is that there are no general rules as to how the traditional terms, Species, Genus, Order, etc. are to be used. Within different groups they have been used differently ; that may be the consequence of genuine differences between the groups, or it may be a consequence of the different whims of investigators. Botanists are quite content with a genus containing 100 species, but zoologists are uneasy when they find more than 20 or 30 in a genus and want to split it up, even though nothing but confusion follows (cf. the high-handed splitting up of that admirable and ancient genus *Pecten*). It has been argued that the species, the smallest stable grouping, is the genuine thing and the larger groupings conventional. Against that many candid observers find just as much difficulty with species as with genera, families, orders or anything else. The amateur naturalist generally feels safer with genera than with species. The puzzles may be at their worst among the more obscure groups of organisms, but there are plenty near at hand with familiar forms.

Nobody can honestly say that the distinction between mice and elephants is purely arbitrary and conventional ; that mice are rather small elephants, or elephants rather large mice, or that both might as well be called cats. These groupings are not arbitrary or conventional in the same way that it is arbitrary and conventional that people who happen to be called Smith happen to live at the house which happens to be called *Mon Repos*, and some who happen to be called Brown happen to live at the house which happens to be called *The Moorings*.

No two sheep are exactly alike but the characters they all share are many and conspicuous, those in which they differ few and less conspicuous. So for any two goats. But any goat resembles any sheep far more closely than either resembles any wolf. Again it is easy to see that any sheep, goat or wolf resembles the others more than it resembles a goose ; and so on. These relations, distinctions and resemblances can not be accused of being purely arbitrary, conventional, subjective, nor called by any other of the rude names used in this connection. Any person who tries to milk a goose or shear a wolf is making a genuine blunder of the most radical sort. He is, if you care to put it that way, defying the laws of nature. It is not the least like ringing the bell at *The Moorings* and asking for Mr. Smith.

So far so good, and simple too ; provided we do not pry into things much further. Above all let us refrain from inquiry about wolves, but do as our ancestors did, shoot them at sight and leave the carcases to be eaten by crows. A few dogs may get shot in the process, but they will have been up to mischief any way. Inquiry into wolves raises difficulties about species. Wolves are, or were, found over the whole of Europe, Asia and North America as far north as the forests extended. Within that area they vary a good deal, in size, colour and thickness of fur, but not structurally. Older taxonomists split them up into 7 or 8 species with different geographical ranges. The tendency now is to lump them all into one species, *Canis lupus*, with local and climatic varieties which remain distinct because they have no opportunity of interbreeding. There are also the jackals. These differ from wolves very little except in size, and between the largest jackal and the smallest wolf there is very little difference at all. Jackals are found in Africa, S. Europe and S. Asia, and their range overlaps that of the smaller wolves. They must be reckoned as belonging to the same genus, *Canis*, but are they a separate species and are there several species of jackal ? Again, the older taxonomists distinguished, apart from the common jackal of Europe and Asia (*C. aureus*), 5 species in Africa and another in India. In N. America there is the Prairie Wolf or Coyote, *C. labians*, very like a jackal, and in Japan a small wolf, again very like a jackal. These may all be just local varieties of one species of jackal. Then there are the foxes and hyenas—but perhaps we had better ignore them ; in any case the taxonomists have tucked them safely away in other genera. The dogs, however, we cannot ignore. Are they hybrids of wolf and jackal, or are they a separate species ? If so, what a species ! Suppose an innocent taxonomist were provided with bones, but no other information, of a number of more extreme varieties ; he would not exclude any from the Family *Canidæ* (cf. Teeth and Feet) but he might well hesitate to put Greyhound, Pug and Dachshund in the same species. Still it may be useful to lump them together into *C. familiaris*, forget about their hypothetical ancestors and say that the extreme forms are pathological. In any case, dogs are practically human artifacts and hardly works of nature. The really difficult species problems are fortunately much fewer than the easy ones and only the very conscientious kind of systematist loses sleep over them. The difficult cases show that rules of taxonomy are complex and awkward in special cases (like human laws) but not that there are no rules at all. The fact that there is a contrast between easy cases and difficult ones, makes things more difficult for the nominalist or conventionalist than for the realist.

§7. After this preliminary, we must go back still further to the statistical notion of a population introduced in Chapter VII, more especially the human illustration of a population of tall men and one of short men. Single out any one measurable character, such as height, and ascertain the frequency with which any value of it occurs, e.g. out of a population of 100,000 find how many are between 6 ft. and 5 ft. 11 ins., how many between 5 ft. 11 ins. and 5 ft. 10 ins., and so on down the scale to the smallest and also up the scale to the tallest. When the frequencies are plotted against the value measured the result is a Frequency Distribution Curve, which in many cases fits the Gaussian formula. Examples are given in Fig. XIII.

A great deal can be seen of what constitutes a population of any sort and of the character of a particular population by direct inspection of the curves and without algebraical complications (which are very complicated). If the curve is symmetrical the distribution of the character in the population is said to be 'normal', though 'undistorted random distribution' might be better. If the curve is skew or deviates from the normal in any other way, the deviation may stand for a significant feature of the population. If we plot the ages of brides or bridegrooms in the United Kingdom, we shall obtain skew curves, which signify that there is a legal minimum age for marriage but no maximum. Similarly, the skew curves, showing the ages at which people die of whooping cough or of cancer, are taken as significant of the way the first disease kills off the young and the second the old (Fig. XIII, C). It is perfectly possible, however, to produce a skew curve by choosing your units in one way and a symmetrical curve by choosing them in another way, e.g. by using a linear scale or a logarithmic one. The practical advantage of obtaining a symmetrical

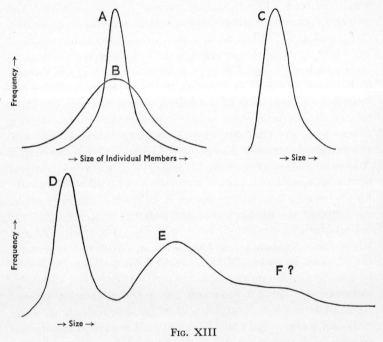

Fig. XIII

A and B are 'normal' curves, for two (imaginary) populations of the same mean size (length or weight) of individual, but B has twice the 'spread' of A.
C is a skew curve; the smaller members of a population such as A are missing.
D and E are recognizably different populations, with overlapping. The wide spread to the right suggests a third population F, not clearly distinguished.

curve is that the arithmetic mean, the intermediate value, coincides with the mode, the most frequent value, so that the distribution is grouped without ambiguity about one centre.

Perhaps the most valuable information supplied by the frequency curve is that in many cases, otherwise dubious, it shows clearly whether it is *one* population grouped about a mean or mode, or *two* or more populations which overlap (Fig. XIII, DEF).

One frequency curve only tells us about a population in terms of one character, but a separate curve can be drawn for any number of characters provided they are measurable in one dimension or else quasi-measurable so that numbers can be assigned by rule (e.g. human intelligence in the terms of the much debated I.Q.). A more serious limitation is that the frequency curve describes only an instantaneous cross section of a population ; it has no time dimension. Consider a human (or plant or animal) population at one time, selected on a basis which includes all ages (e.g. all inhabitants of the County of Rutland at the 1951 Census), and not on an exclusive age basis (e.g. all members of the British armed forces at the same time). In Rutland there will be representatives of at least 4 generations, (1) children, (2) parents and others of like age, (3) grandparents and others of like age, (4) a few older still. An instantaneous cross section conceals or distorts this temporal depth. A complete survey of a population should be historical ; for that reason a complete survey is difficult if not impossible. The further we go back into the past the more blurred our boundaries of populations become. This is specially obvious when the boundaries are geographical. Rutland is a rural county with only two small towns and the population there may be assumed to be more stable than in an industrial and large town area. For all that not all grandparents of present Rutlanders lived in Rutland and of great grandparents fewer still, and so on. We can be sure that if we could inquire far enough back into the past we should come to a time when no ancestors of the present population lived in Rutland. So also, *mutatis mutandis*, for other populations whatever their boundaries. The argument would still apply if we possessed the fullest possible historical records. These we conspicuously do not possess, for human populations or any others.

If complete surveys in historical depth are out of the question, partial and sampling surveys are not so difficult, and do at least show how far populations are stable or unstable wherever they are available. Let us take the extreme and general case.

As has been mentioned, a survey of the whole fossil record shows that in the long run no animal population is quite stable, though a few animal forms have changed very little.* Fossils of certain Brachiopods and Molluscs differing hardly at all from species now living have been found in late Cambrian rocks. Of course, these are bottom-living marine organisms which have the advantage of an environment which changes very little, even in several million years, and therefore there is less inducement for such forms to change. In spite of that, many old types of marine organisms have died out, and many new types have appeared. But apart from the fishes, which are new, all the main large groups of animals (such groups as Crustaceans, Molluscs, Brachiopods, Echinoderms, Coelenterates) are found among the earliest fossils. Sweeping generalizations to the effect that older types are ill-adapted and newer types better adapted are unwarranted. If it is true that the unicellular organisms are the most ancient of all, then, among these, the Flagellates have probably the best claim to seniority. They now swarm in every sea ; there are many species, and they do not look in the least obsolete. Still, the vertebrates are genuine newcomers and are in most places dominant forms. Yet they have not ousted older forms, and on land, in the tropics, it takes them all their time to hold their own against the insects.

If any general conclusion is attempted it must be stated cautiously and not too simply. In the very long run change and instability is the rule, but it is not so visible in the shorter run, certainly not in a few thousand years. If the time scale of the modern biologist were as short as Aristotle's he would uphold the fixity of species with Aristotle. It is an oversimplification, but at the beginning oversimplification is a help, even if it may become a hindrance later. If biologists had begun by worrying about overlapping forms, incomplete segregation and instability of species they would never have got anywhere ; above all they would never have acquired enough information to challenge initial assumptions, whether good or bad or on one side or the other. In any natural science, physical or biological, the necessary methodical rule

* What is said here about animal populations applies, I suppose, to the more difficult case of plant populations.

is to look for constancy and stability first, and when something of that sort has been found to look for order in change by referring the change to stable factors. Only as a last resort, when the Heavenly Powers fail, should the devotee turn to the demons of the Underworld, Chance and Probability.

A species is (1) an assemblage of similar forms, with (2) a history. If we are lucky we have no difficulty about the meaning of ' similar '. If we are not, our specific name may be a convention in part, but not entirely. *Canis familiaris* is about the most dubious of all species known to man and *Homo sapiens* the next most dubious. Nevertheless there are some useful working generalizations to be made about dogs and men. There is no need to brood over the difficulties of deciding when a species is a ' good ' one or not. There is no need either to be too gloomy over the difficulties raised by histories (2). However, (3) a species has a determinate environment. This means a great many different things. It means first of all that the members of the species are found living in certain places, where they find conditions that are suited to them, and not in other places of a different sort. In short, every species has a territory (if we may speak of marine or aquatic territories) or a geographical range. This may be wide ; for instance Man and the Peregrine Falcon are found all over the land surface of the globe wherever life is possible. Other species of land animals have a more limited range. Some species, or at least sub-species, are confined to one small island. There are land plants confined to one patch of a few square yards, or several isolated patches. There are birds, large and powerful flyers too, which range over a wide area outside the breeding season but breed only in a few very restricted areas. A restricted territory may indicate a dying species, or else a new, up and coming species, or it may indicate no more than some oddity in behaviour. Questions about territory and specially about change of territory raise many pretty problems, some so pretty that they are unlikely ever to be solved. The sea— in which conditions are more stable and uniform than on land and in which movement is, in principle, free in all directions— provides the prettiest of all.

A final consideration (4) is that a species centres round a

type. The type admits of variation in several directions ; it even admits of abnormality. A *type* is less rigid than a *specification* (a term discussed below, §8). It is in short the Aristotelian *Form*, which I take to be the biological counterpart of the mathematical Platonic *Form*.

Mrs. Arber in her book *The Natural Philosophy of Plant Form*, (1950) discusses this whole question in a most illuminating way, specially in Chapters V and VI. She quotes a pregnant saying of William Whewell (*Philosophy of the Inductive Sciences*, Vol. I, p. 476). He points out that a natural class of objects ' is determined, not by a boundary line without, but by a central point within ; not by what it strictly excludes, but by what it eminently includes ; by an example not by a precept ; in short, instead of a Definition, we have a type for our director '.* Mrs Arber points out that Whewell failed to develop the implications of his statement, which is of necessity ' idealist ' (in one way or another). Philosophical idealism of any sort was as unfashionable in England (though it had a foothold in Scotland) in the 1840's as in the 1940's. However we are to take the notion, Mrs. Arber again has the pregnant quotation, Spinoza's account of *conatus* (*Ethics*, Part III, Prop. 7). ' The effort by which each thing endeavours to persevere in its own being is nothing but the actual essence of the thing itself.' Before going further two short digressions may perhaps be allowed.

(a) As to history : a species in the concrete as it lives is ' a historic route of occasions' in Whitehead's terminology. It has been and is a set of happenings throughout an epoch of time and an extent of space. It is identified collectively by the similarity of organic forms displayed and also certain continuities of inorganic nature within that stretch of time and space. For instance, all human history, including archæology, taken together with all statistical information, geographical, political and social about human populations is as much as is known about the human species collectively and concretely. This mass of information is full of gaps ; it is in many places

---

* The *a*, *β*, *γ* system of marking in examinations is based on the *type* concept of a typical 1st, 2nd, or 3rd Class candidate (at least in its original form). The percentage mark depends upon *defining* the upper and lower limit of the 3 classes.

inaccurate and conjectural ; the whole of it is too much for anybody to grasp. We have to deal with it by means of abstractions to cut out complications, above all to cut out historical complications by taking cross sections of what is happening during short periods. We attain precision by abstraction, at a price ; sometimes at the price of talking nonsense. And it is abstractions that cause the quarrels between enthusiasts of the philosophical schools ; Realists, Conceptualists, Nominalists, Conventionalists, Old Uncle Tom Cobley and all.

(b) Lord Russell and the Logicians who follow him assume that there is a pure logic of classes which owes nothing to any actual usage. Outside the realm of living forms and of artifacts, which are by-products of the organic realm and which include geometrical figures and numbers, there are no classes. The logician or mathematician can properly abstract from the biological nature of classes but he cannot abstract from their spatial nature. A member of a class is recognized as such by means of, at the least, spatial (or temporal) form which provides the connotation of the class name. Its location in space and time gives the denotation. The Russellian calculus of propositions (so-called) might conceivably be pure logic if logic could be pure ; the calculus of classes and that of relations cannot be anything but impure logic.

§8. I have attempted to indicate, or at least hint at, the problems that face the student of the natural history of living organisms. From the earliest days, certainly from Aristotle onwards, such students have been tempted to compare living organisms with human artifacts, machines, and many have been misled by the comparison. Yet it is useful and even necessary, because all artifacts are consequences of organic activity. The comparison is misleading only when it is forgotten that living organisms are natural and artifacts artificial. Because artifacts have been made by us, their ' nature ' or ' essence ' is open to our inspection, while that of organisms is not. ' Reason has insight only into that which it produces after a plan of its own ' ; i.e. into artifacts such as those of geometry and chemistry as Kant points out. Artifacts

Copper Beeches in all gardens, parks and avenues all over the world are cuttings from one original wild specimen found in the Black Forest more than 200 years ago.

Even among annual plants, where one seed gives rise to one physically separate specimen, it can be claimed that these are not individuals. It can be argued that where a number of seeds are grown which are all genetically homogeneous, then the plants will be all alike, except so far as external causal factors have affected them differently. The factors are those of soil, water, temperature, sunlight, parasites and diseases ; and they can be specified in some detail, though rarely in complete detail. The argument depends upon invoking a hypothetical and possibly fabulous external factor wherever any difference in growth is observed, in order to explain away the difference. I think we can quote some quite familiar evidence against the argument. Consider an avenue or row of deciduous trees, e.g. Limes or Common Elms, from cuttings from one original, and thus genetically homogeneous. As they are grown together, soil, water, temperature and sunlight conditions will all be closely similar, and probability of attack by parasites and diseases not so different ; at any rate if one is attacked it is likely that several will be. Yet it is often noticed that the trees do not all come into leaf simultaneously. Sometimes .one of them persistently buds earlier (or later) than the majority. There may also be divergencies in flowering and fruiting. Those who want to explain everything away can do it here in terms of a hypothetical *virus* or else of a cutting from another source that has slipped in by accident. If cuttings were taken from the variant tree and grown along with some from the others and the variation found to persist it would be interesting but it would not refute the anti-individualist argument ; nor would the opposite result establish it. It does remain that this kind of behaviour is suggestive ; the plant may within its limits be displaying individuality ; variety with order, not just random variety. There are also cases of idiosyncrasy in form, which can be taken in this way and are not to be dismissed off-hand as pathological or random. (Cf. A. Arber, *Natural Philosophy of Plant Form*, 1950, pp. 51-58, 109-111, 187-189.)

[151]

In this connection it is best to forget the common distinction between plants and animals, so conspicuous among the higher forms of both sorts, but inconspicuous among the lower forms. The higher plants are sessile and thus can *do* nothing but grow and reproduce. Any variety of conduct has to be displayed within these narrow limits. The higher animals move about in search of food or mates or to escape enemies, and in this have abundant scope for variety. Among the humbler organisms plants may be free-swimming and animals sessile.

The Flagellates are unicellular organisms which are strong competitors for the prize for the Most Primitive Living Type. (The Blue-green Algæ are likely to run them close, if Bacteria are disqualified as degenerate.) At any rate they are of simple structure and they swarm in all the seas and in fresh water too ; e.g. *Euglena* which is common in ponds and ditches. Most Flagellates are plant-like but some are animal-like, and there are species, specimens of which may be either. The plant-like forms are green with chlorophyll and also free-swimming, propelling themselves with the whips, or *flagellæ* from which they take their name. The animal-like forms have no chlorophyll, but a kind of mouth and gullet. They are usually fixed to a solid surface and propel small particles towards their mouths with their flagellæ. Here it is the animal that lives the restricted life and the plant which has fuller scope.

Many of the marine invertebrates, undoubted animals, do not live as separate ' individuals ' but as colonies produced by vegetable multiplication ; e.g. Sponges, Hydroids, colonial Tunicates (*Botryllus*, and the like). Some solitary Sea Anemones too reproduce vegetatively. All these forms are sessile, and of those named only Sea Anemones are capable of moving about at all. There are also solitary animals which reproduce sexually only and are sessile, completely immovable or only occasionally moving. The Barnacles for instance are not capable of movement in adult life, once the free-swimming larvæ have settled. Among the Bivalve Molluscs there is every variety. The Oysters are quite immovable once the larvæ have settled. The Common Mussel (*Mytilus*) in the adult form is found attached to some solid object between tide marks by a bunch of stout threads (the *byssus*). If it is detached it can move itself a little by means of its small, poorly developed *foot* and can reattach itself by spinning a new *byssus*. The Common Cockle (*Cardium*) is generally found in a burrow in the sand, but it can come out and it skips about actively in the water with the help of a large muscular foot. The Scallops can all swim freely, some of them very actively indeed, e.g. the small *Pecten opercularis* (or *Chlamys opercularis* as they insist on calling it). Other species spin a *byssus* and are found attached at some stage of their lives.

One would suppose off-hand (or *a priori*) that of these four types it would be the permanently fixed oyster that would display the least variability or individuality. That is not so. The mussels are the animals that have shown the most uniform and well-drilled behaviour, and it has been made the basis of purifying mussels from contaminated waters and rendering them fit to eat. You have only to put mussels in clean aerated sea water at a suitable temperature and they will all open and pump the water through themselves, so clearing out bacteria, debris, etc. If the temperature is below a certain minimum they all close with complete unanimity. Oysters, on the other hand, are most difficult to purify as they are more individualistic; while most of them are open and pumping, a recalcitrant minority are apt to remain shut. This is perhaps surprising, though I think one can look for the explanation in two directions (taken together, not as incompatibles, though one is mechanistic, the other teleological). The mussel's nervous system is less centralized than the oyster's and therefore more closely confined to automatic invariable responses to stimuli. Secondly, the ' needs ' of the animals are different according to their different environment. The mussel lives between tide marks and it is only when the tide is up and covering it that it can open and pump water for feeding and even for breathing. When the tide is down it has to keep tight shut to conserve its ' body water ' and keep moist. The oyster lives below low water mark and has all day and all night to breathe and feed. On the other hand it is more liable to be attacked by predatory animals, and shutting its valves is its sole defence.

It is not at all surprising that the scallops, which have a nervous system of a pattern like the oyster's and very elaborate sensory organs (for molluscs) and also are free-swimming, have conspicuous individualistic tendencies.

The moral of this story is that an organism will show just as much individuality as it can under its circumstances, that is according to (a) its environment, (b) its basic needs, (c) its physiological make up. The more elaborate (c) is, the *higher* the organism in the scale, according to ordinary reckoning, and the greater the variety of its behaviour, within the limits set by (a) and (b). Individuality is therefore not so easy to see low down in the scale, but it may be there *if it is looked for*. Again, by individuality I mean variety of behaviour without destruction of an orderly pattern, not just random or disorderly behaviour. The conception is made difficult because of a certain ambiguity underlying the motion of *order* and even worse ambiguity underlying notions of *chance* or *randomness*. In the lifeless physical realm we can and must always ignore what happens infrequently in favour of what happens ' for the most part ', and our criteria are statistical or mass criteria ; in the organic realm ignoring of this kind is not permissible ; we cannot afford to ignore either the infrequent or the frequent. Mass behaviour, what happens for the most part is of course significant, *for the group* ; but what happens only occasionally, or very seldom even, is significant *for the individual*. In a word among organisms there are individuals, elsewhere only crowds. Individuality, like every other advantage has to be paid for. For men the price is fear and greed, at the best ; at the worst complete self absorption (cf. Dante, *Inferno*, Canto 34.).

CHAPTER IX

HUMAN ORDER

Prediction in human and other studies · No single human science · Special human sciences · Evidence in law and history · Medical digression · Lessons from Aristotle's Politics · Prediction and morals

§1. GENUINE sciences are expected to justify themselves in practice. After a preliminary probationary period, during which queer things may happen, they succeed in doing so. All sciences are supposed to begin with past events, with facts ; but some go on to experiment and predict. Experimental sciences justify themselves by orderly control of events, i.e. by introducing order into otherwise chaotic processes. In doing this they may be said to predict, but their predictions are confined, with rare exceptions, to the four walls of the laboratory (Latin) or workshop (Anglo-Saxon) from which they come and to which they refer. Prediction outside laboratories and workshops is more precarious though not impossible (cf. R. O. Kapp, *Facts and Faith*, 1955. Riddell Lectures).

Consider the science of meteorology. The weather is assumed to be a purely physical process, the laws of classical physics are assumed to apply to these processes. Indeed the meteorologist habitually uses some of these laws for his calculations, e.g. for calculating the deviation of wind direction due to the earth's rotation and the cooling or heating of air masses in rising or descending air currents ; these are some of his tools, just as barometers and thermometers are. For his predictions however, he uses imaginative entities unknown to classical physics, whose relations are discovered by him empirically, independently of physical theory. Such are his cyclonic and anti-cyclonic systems, and warm and cold fronts. His predictions are not at all like the predictions of the physicist about what goes on in his laboratory but they are very like the predictions of the botanist about what goes on in the countryside. Show the botanist an acorn and a broad bean, and he will predict what will become of each, when planted under suitable conditions, and specify the characters of the full grown plants in great detail and with complete confidence, provided only they do grow and reach maturity. The poor meteorologist is not nearly so confident as the botanist, but for all that he does predict. Let us see why he is different.

By tossing a coin you can predict tomorrow's weather with 50% success as long as you stick to plain opposites, wet or dry, warm or cold. By the still simpler method of saying that tomorrow's weather will be like today's you can attain more than 50% successes, something like 60%. On the other hand by this method you will miss all the changes in the weather, and for many human purposes these are important. (The coin tossing method errs in the other direction ; it predicts too many changes.) The expert using all available techniques is very lucky if he achieves 70% successful predictions, *on the average*. But averages are very misleading things. The expert will very seldom miss the dangerous changes, the storms, though he may overestimate or underestimate them or be a bit wrong about the exact time. He predicts in considerable detail, therefore takes bigger risks.

In all these cases of prediction it is ' for the most part ', not ' universally ' nor ' of necessity '. Thus a statistical element comes in. Prediction is of the group rather than of the individual. The botanist for example is happier if you show him a thousand acorns, not one only, and also tell him how you propose to deal with them, and where you got them from. Then he will predict what will happen to 95% of them or perhaps even 99%. Here we see how the experimental and statistical merge, and also how they can be used in open air, not in the air-conditioned laboratory.

An excellent comment has been made by Larmor, a theoretical physicist, and nothing has transpired since to invalidate it. He said : ' The observable regularities of nature belong to statistical molecular phenomena, which have settled down to permanent stable conditions. In so far as weather may be due to an unlimited assemblage of local instabilities it may not be amenable to a finite scheme at all.' (Quoted by Sir David Brunt, *Science Progress* 1956, Vol. 44, p. 205.) In short some types of weather may be inherently unpredictable, and not just unpredicted by us who have not yet collected sufficient data. For instance, westerly air streams over the British Isles give the familiar ' scattered showers and bright intervals '. Nobody knows where the rain will fall nor how much (though, vaguely, more on hills less on low ground), nor where the sun will shine nor how long ; there is no reason to suppose that anybody ever will know. In contrast, there is a stable, predictable type of weather such as belongs for most of the year to Trade Wind latitudes.

In meteorology we attribute unpredictability to chance or instability of certain sorts, because we have nothing else to which to attribute it. Suppose, however, we knew that the weather was controlled by a Grand Committee of Demons, malicious but not efficient. If we had no further information that much would make no difference. But if a reporter were present at committee meetings and could tell us how the discussion went, our predictions would often be more successful and for longer periods, when there was a large majority of the committee in favour of some definite policy, either floods, or drought not both. But if he reported that the demons were all at sixes and sevens things would be exactly as they are now. Introducing a factor of choice, demonic or human, may make the situation more predictable not less, but predictable in terms of desires, motives, volitions, as well as in physical terms.

Positivists have pointed out, correctly, that the laws of the physical world are not *prescriptions* as to how nature must or should behave, but are general *descriptions* of how in fact it does behave. Positivists seldom take the further step of remembering that they who formulate these laws are human as well as just ' natural ' and could not have thought of the descriptive laws unless they themselves operated in accordance with their own prescriptive laws. Every descriptive law takes shelter behind a prescriptive one. There are different kinds of order, complementary not incompatible.

The psychologist can predict some human behaviour, not all. The botanist can predict some plant behaviour, not all ; and predicts with more confidence than the psychologist. Both of these can predict with more confidence than the meteorologist, though he deals with purely physical processes.

None of the three predict by the methods of the experimental physicist.

§2. So much for genuine sciences. Now a word about bogus ones. Alchemy can be dismissed as a science because no alchemist ever turned lead into gold or even silver.*

As to astrology, the early Mesopotamians predicted eclipses, claiming thereby to avert public disasters which would follow unpredicted eclipses. After this dubious early success no other successes have been reported in spite of innumerable astrologers predicting innumerable events. No event of public importance has ever been predicted by an astrologer *before* it happened. *Afterwards*, they have consulted their horoscopes and said that they could have predicted it had they had a mind to. One notable failure was the 'Great Conjunction' of February 11, 1524, when all the planets assembled in the constellation *Pisces*. Universal deluges and other disasters were predicted, but that day turned out to be like any other day in any February. This failure is probably historically important as marking the beginning of the descent of astrology from the courts of kings to the pages of the Sunday newspapers.

We may perhaps take astrology to be the first attempt at a comprehensive science of sociology, and as a bad omen for those who would model sociology on the physical sciences. Yet when these sciences attained their modern prestige it was, in a way, natural to make new attempts at physical or quasi-physical sociology. Hobbes seems to have been the first to try. Hard things have been said about him, not all of them fair. Hobbes is of permanent importance because, with his robust common sense, he drew attention to certain unpleasant aspects of human life, which many well-meaning people like to forget. He is not of importance as the founder of a science or for anything he said about the supposed physical character or physical

---

* The epitaph of alchemy appeared at the right moment in history in *The Beggar's Opera*. The highwaymen sing : 'See this ball I hold ! Let chemists toil like asses, Our fire their fire surpasses And turns all our lead to gold.'

Perhaps I should add that Alchemy and Astrology are both convicted of obtaining money under false pretences ; other bogus sciences so far only of the misdemeanour of pedantry. Yet the career of Marxism shows what may happen when pedants are given political power.

causation of human thoughts, desires, emotions and so on ; though many have repeated Hobbist doctrines since, even up to the present day. There is still no more science in them than there was at the beginning.

What has been said about Hobbes may also be said about the similar theories of the French Enlightenment of the 18th century and similar ones of the 19th. These last were the most ambitious, flamboyant and least excusable efforts to produce ' scientific ' sociology in imitation of physical science ; namely those of Auguste Comte (who invented the name), Karl Marx and Herbert Spencer. The first criticism to be made is that if we take the three theories together they pretty well cancel out, and this is precisely what they should not do if they are scientific and about the same subject, as they claim to be. The second criticism, if a second is required, is that all three smell of the midnight oil and the ivory tower. They none of them have the proper smell of places where collective or public human action occurs, where discussion goes on and decisions are made. They do not belong to the family hearth, the farm, the workshop, the market, the law courts, the legislative chamber, nor yet the battlefield.* Marx could claim to be a journalist and politician and had more foundation to his studies than Comte who taught mathematics or Spencer who was an engineer in a small way for a short time.

Nobody now reads the works of Comte or Spencer. It is hard to believe that they were ever found readable. They scarcely even appear in modern bibliographies. In short, they are dead. Yet 60 years ago Spencer's books were read all over the world in many languages by thousands of devoted disciples. Comte was never so popular, but at one time had many disciples, some of whom were men of intellectual distinction. The work of Marx is quite as dead, but his bones were disinterred in 1917 and jerked into a semblance of life, when Lenin proclaimed his outrageous fiction that the Russian Revolution of that year was the Social Revolution predicted

---

* It is not that the decisions of the battlefield are good or constructive, but that they are apt to be final. The dialectic or discussion that makes up normal collective and public life may end in war, civil or international ; a fact not to be ignored by the theorist even if he thinks he knows better than Hobbes.

by Marx, and that he and his friends were the sole, genuine, 100% Marxists. At this late date it should not be necessary to refute these 19th century claims in more detail.

There are newer 20th century claims, not so flamboyant, nor so comprehensive, nor so crudely quasi-physical and thus not so easily refuted. Professor W. J. H. Sprott has reviewed a number of them.* He is not a hostile witness ; he makes the best he can of the material he discusses, but he cannot make a coherent body of knowledge out of miscellaneous prejudices dressed up to look like science. Above all he cannot make academic small beer taste like strong ale. He cannot conceal that persistent sociological vice, the attitude of the Superior Person. The writers are all immaculate and omniscient, examining from above the turmoil of the anthill the absurd antics of the ants. It is a short step from the snobbery of the Superior Person to the criminal intent of the Commissar, who sets out to eliminate any antics he considers absurd, and liquidate unruly ants. These fallacies are not entirely new. There is quite a bit of the Superior Person about Plato, though less than hostile critics make out and compensated for by other features which hostile critics ignore.

If there were to be one comprehensive science of human life, character, action and so on, it could not operate, as do the physical sciences, on terms of ' limited liability ', or to put it another way, within ' a closed circle of Ideas '. The physical scientist begins by saying : ' I am going to examine this kind of thing in this kind of way, therefore I rule out everything else and every other procedure as irrelevant.' He generally forgets to add the three final words ' to my purpose ' ; for apart from human purposes there is no relevance or irrelevance. At any rate this is how he simplifies and limits his problems, also simplifying and limiting his point of view. There could be no such process of limiting the liability or closing the circle in a comprehensive study of man (or men), for the comprehensive investigator needs to include himself in his own investigation (cf. J. Macmurray, *The Boundaries of Science*, Faber, 1939).

---

* *Science and Social Action*, 1954. Much more radical criticism comes from the U.S.A. P. A. Sorokin, *Fad and Foibles in Modern Sociology and Related Sciences*, Chicago, 1956.

This is the first and undeniable difficulty. The second is greater but often denied to be a difficulty at all or even to exist. It is that man is, in Sir Thomas Browne's phrase, the Great Amphibian. The investigator may choose to investigate only the submerged portion of the creature, but that is an irrational and self-stultifying choice. It is not the kind of restrictive choice that is made on legitimate technical grounds. Those who make it do so in order to shut out what they do not like. If there were to be a comprehensive sociology, or science of man under any other name, it would have to include or to be theology. Anybody who thinks that this is just propaganda for Christian orthodoxy should consult Aristotle, who cannot be accused of this kind of propaganda. In the *Ethics* he discusses the question : What is the chief end of man ? and answers it in terms like those of the Shorter Catechism of the Church of Scotland.

§3. Suppose then we abandon for the time being the project which so far has always ended in failure, and look instead for a number of special and limited sciences dealing with special and specially orderly aspects of human life and therefore able to claim limited liability. The advantage of this procedure is that such sciences actually exist and some are old and quite respectable with nothing bogus about them at all. Consider first a newcomer, born, according to usual reckoning, in the 18th century ; namely Economics. She has survived the ailments of infancy and is now a healthy growing child. Economics owes her success to her strict attention to business. She confines herself to one set of human aims and activities, namely the production and exchange of ' goods '. ' Goods ' are in the first instance material objects, like food and clothing, that can be produced and exchanged by deliberate action and are useful as means of life. The class of ' goods ' includes, secondarily, human activities needed for production and exchange; labour and various kinds of services. Thus a fire insurance policy must be reckoned among economic goods. Sound natural teeth cannot be reckoned among economic ' goods ', though they are good things to possess. False teeth, whether sound or not, do count as economic ' goods ' even though, after the first exchange their exchange value is small. The difference is that the second are produced and exchanged, the first are not. It is not a fallacy for the economist to ignore good things that are not producible by labour or exchangeable ; it is a necessary technical limitation. Without such a limitation economics would be idle speculation at best, or at worst an attempt to obtain money under false pretences. Economics can now hold her head up, in spite of her tender years and some shakiness on the theoretical side, alongside of her older sisters, Law and Medicine. Each of these deals with a different and determinate human aim ; the one with preserving public order and justice, the other with preserving health, private and public.*

These sciences though all human are sometimes supposed to be unrelated, but that is clearly not so, if we add a fourth to the group, Politics. Politics is related quite obviously to Law, and also to Economics in the modern world. When medicine was taken to be concerned with private persons only it seemed unrelated to Politics ; but the study of public health might almost be called political medicine. It is perhaps unfortunate that the term ' political ' is so often used as a term of abuse, but not unnatural when one remembers the history of the terms ' alchemy ' and ' chemistry '.

There is no better way of starting to discuss the subject of Politics then to use the earliest textbook, Aristotle's work of that name. This is not to disparage Plato ; only to recognize that Plato wrote no textbook. Aristotle is factual, sober, cautious and, within the limits of his resources, systematic ; he is all those things that scientists are supposed to be, and many later exponents of sociology are not. It is no grave defect in him that he dealt only with the Greek city state, nor that when he did so it was already moribund. On his very reasonable view the important thing about the Greeks and their cities

* Economic science, because it is human, faces certain difficulties of a special kind. (1) Because many people suppose that money is real wealth and act on this supposition, a pure fiction acquires a quasi-reality. (2) Following on this nearly all buyers think that prices are too high and nearly all sellers think that prices are too low. As long as such a view prevails there can be no complete reconciliation of interests on purely economic grounds without the introduction of other grounds outside the economic.

was that policy was there discussed and argued about. Greeks were not entirely subject to blind custom nor compelled in blind obedience by despots. Outside the Hellenic world he could see these two alternatives of barbarism and slavery operating, and nothing that could be called politics, any more than in an anthill or beehive.

About what went on inside the Hellenic world Aristotle was well informed, by natural process, by living within it, without having recourse to Blue Books or other works of reference, which were happily non-existent. There was nothing to hinder his taking an extensive and synoptic view of the affairs of his generation, and doing so with sufficient accuracy for his purpose. The communities he knew were small and compact, life was lived and business done in the open, in the public view, easily grasped by any intelligent onlooker. We must reckon Aristotle, citizen of a small, remote (but not undisturbed) city, who lived most of his life elsewhere, as onlooker more than participant, nevertheless a well placed onlooker, detached in the good rather than the bad sense. To add to his own and his friends' more direct acquaintance with affairs he took the trouble to compile with them the con-stitutional histories of 158 city states (part of the characteristic Aristotelian effort to initiate our now vast *corpus* of works of reference). This compilation formed the basis of a theory of a modest and useful kind, embodied in the middle books of the *Politics*, those which may be called 'The Statesman's Handbook'. No statesman of the present day would be the worse for studying it. It is rather more up to date than Machiavelli or Hobbes and much more up to date than Comte, Marx or Spencer.

As a preliminary to Aristotle we must consider a great obstacle to political science at the present day, namely that the modern world and its life do not lie open to any intelligent onlooker. Things are hidden, scattered, remote, or else too highly centralized. They are buried under piles of paper, only to be discovered bit by bit by laborious and specialized techniques. Those who ' strictly meditate the thankless Muse ' of Statistics * do what they can to collect information

* It is not yet sufficiently realised that the original Nine were given powers to co-opt.

and reduce it to intelligible form, but the work is difficult, expensive and, above all, slow. By the time the data are available they are often ancient history, the state of affairs to which they refer will never recur. Even information which is not seriously out of date is often inaccurate, misleading and may even be deliberately falsified (this was not unknown in the ancient world). Modern statesmen spend much of their time locking stable doors behind stolen horses and wishing they lived in the happy-go-lucky days when nobody knew where the stables were, and horses looked after themselves.

Still, information is there, specially a new and useful kind for the administrator and legislator, statistical information about large groups. For the first time in history the consequences of political action on the population taken collectively can be discovered. Except to a small extent in financial matters which supply their own statistics, no ruler before the 19th century had more than a very vague idea of the consequences of any action. Still, even statistical information needs to be collected systematically, handled accurately, and used honestly. The first thing we need to know about any alleged information is whether it can be relied upon. Curiously enough students of politics have seldom asked this question; perhaps they believed in the infallibility of the printed word. However, lawyers and historians have asked the question and have made the necessary first steps in the direction of scientific treatment.

We should distinguish two kinds of evidence or information, firstly that which is obtained by direct confrontation of persons, the kind chiefly used by Aristotle and other early writers, and secondly that which is indirect, mostly written. It might be useful to employ the term evidence for the first kind and information for the other, but it would be contrary to ordinary use and pedantic to try to make such a general rule where confusion hardly ever arises. Both lawyers and historians speak of evidence and mostly lawyers deal with the first kind and historians with the second.

There is a difficulty about written evidence which accounts for the suspicions of modern courts of law, and was in part voiced by Socrates long ago. Written words do not vouch for their own good faith, accuracy or meaning. All this has to be done for them, preferably by direct questioning of a living witness, who may be able to tell us who wrote them, when, with what intentions, whether he was honest, well informed, clear and accurate in expression. By questioning we can discover all these things about the person questioned and indirectly about other people too, if he is the right person to ask. As to the last of these points, accuracy of expression : if a written document is obscure, confused and incomplete there is no remedy unless the writer can be questioned directly. When a person is questioned directly he may at first be obscure, confused, and tell only part of his story ; but under suitable questioning can remedy all these defects to a greater or less extent ; indeed it may be possible to extract from him more than he ever knew he had. In dealing with old documents, and such bits of material evidence as may survive, there is no very great difficulty as long as they all corroborate each other ; apart from the difficulty that the documents may appear to corroborate simply because they are all copies of one original. If they fail to corroborate, or worse still contradict, then we know that somebody has forgotten something or somebody has not told the truth ; but beyond that negative information we know nothing. If the chronicler says that Lord X died in bed of heart failure at the age of 80, and the well known monument to Lord X is found to contain a skeleton of a man of 40 with a large dent in the skull, then either we must doubt the veracity of the chronicler or the identification of the body in the tomb ; but we do not know what Lord X died of nor at what age, and are never likely to know. But if the historian has to remain ignorant of many details he does sometimes have another resort, a vague, indefinite, but often reliable knowledge of the general trend of events, or general probabilities. Let us consider in order three points raised in this preliminary discussion ; behaviour of witnesses, corroboration of documents and other material evidence, the general trend of events.

§4. Courts of law are liable to be concerned mainly, even entirely, with problems of honesty and reliability of witnesses, as originators or initiators, not as mere transmitters ; as

persons, not as machines. In claims for compensation for
injury or for breach of contract it is assumed that the two
parties will tell a different story, that both stories cannot be
entirely true and both may be entirely false. If that were not
so there would be nothing for the court to decide. Testimony
on either side may conflict with that on the other, because (1)
of ill-intention or deliberate lying, (2) ill-information, a
witness may be misinformed, or confused, (3) pure myopia, he
may take a partial view of the situation out of ignorance,
without dishonesty. From the behaviour of witnesses in court
it is hoped to discover (1) how honest they are, (2) how well
informed, (3) how complete their view may be, in that order.
At the beginning there is probably nobody in the court who
has a complete view. At the end of the proceedings everybody
in the court should have a complete view, so that justice is done
and manifestly seen to be done. The history of courts of appeal
shows that one should not be too optimistic about the universal
attainment of the ideal, though sometimes something like it is
attained. The important point to notice here is simply that
(3) does come last, if at all.

What comes first is (1) to discover who is telling the truth
and who is lying. Sometimes nothing else needs to be known
or can be known. If two motor cars have collided head on
in the middle of the road and there are no witnesses but the
two drivers, it is generally possible to discover which is the
bigger liar and to decide in favour of the other, even though
the bigger liar may have been at the time the less culpable
party. It is not however entirely a matter of deliberate lying,
reliability is needed as well as honesty. Mr. A may be well-
intentioned, but vague, with a poor memory and no capacity
for clear, coherent, full expression, so that for all his honesty
he is a poor witness. Mr. B may be dishonest in intention, but
have a good memory, and be able to describe events or
situations fully and accurately. Skilfully handled he may be
a more valuable witness than poor A.

Next comes (2) : the court has to collect information about
events that have taken place or situations that exist more or
less permanently, like trade customs. This information can
come from an immense variety of sources, but in the first

instance from what is actually said by witnesses about events within their own experience, for though all such enquiry is into history, most legal enquiry is into recent history. The archetype of all historical information is :—' At 9.30 p.m. on the night in question I saw the accused in such a place doing so and so.' Everything else is derivative, second-hand, third-hand or worse ; or else of the nature of a mnemonic. But mnemonics need to be interpreted and a living witness is needed to do that. This is most obvious in the case of ' material' evidence, e.g. the blunt instrument produced in court with blood and hair sticking to it. Also, as is obvious in this case, without scientific theory and actual examination of that object by a scientific expert the object itself would not tell anybody anything ; the blood and hair must be identified as human (or as non-human), and should, if that is possible, be identified as those of the victim (or else as those of somebody else). And this question of the identity of persons is a very tricky one.

As generally presented to a court of law, this probem (2) is a matter of accumulating detail until there is a sufficient body of coherent details to establish a definite story, and no sufficient body of conflicting evidence to throw doubt upon that story. If this is successfully accomplished then a view of the case should emerge which is synoptic or complete in outline (no view is completely complete) and not merely partial or myopic. But this is the really awkward problem. A great accumulation of very precise and reliable detail does not necessarily provide any synoptic view; not because of any defect in any detail but because of gaps which cannot be filled in, of mere lack of evidence. On the other hand there are situations, where in spite of lack of detail and in spite of conflicting and unreliable detail, there is a synoptic view which cannot be seriously doubted. The jurist is more often faced with the first difficulty—plenty of detail but no synoptic view. The historian, and specially the ancient historian, is more often faced with the second—few and unreliable details but something of a synoptic view.

For the jurist's difficulty let me quote the famous trial of Madeleine Smith (1857), where the verdict was Not Proven, the only reasonable conclusion, given the evidence before the

court or, I would venture to say, any evidence that could
have been brought before the court. A great many people at
the time and since have believed that she was guilty, but that
belief has been based more on prejudice than on evidence.
The case for the Prosecution was that she had poisoned her
discarded lover Emile L'Angelier with arsenic ; but, though
she had openly purchased arsenic (3 oz. of white arsenic
altogether ; enough to kill a couple of hundred Guardsmen,
not to mention one small man in poor health) the Lord
Advocate completely failed to show how, on the night that he
was poisoned, she could have administered to him the very
large quantity of arsenic found in his body after death. The
argument in her defence was that Emile had committed
suicide, but it failed to show why he should have done so then,
in that way, or that he possessed arsenic to do it with. There
are gaps in both stories that render both improbable, though
the suicide version is rather less improbable than the murder
version. It is easy to believe either story if you look at the gaps
in the other and forget the gaps in your own ; or else fill them
in with ' somehow or other something of the sort must have
happened ' ; a formula often called upon to do a great deal
of hard work.

For the historian's difficulty, the Battle of Marathon provides
a good example. The sole near-contemporary evidence comes
from Herodotus. Later writers, whose work survives, give
little detail and probably Herodotus was their source. He
was born at Halicarnassus in the year of Marathon or possibly
in the year of Salamis. At any rate he was too young to be
an eyewitness, nor was he very expert in military affairs,
unlike Thucydides. He had to rely on hearsay evidence picked
up many years later and most of it little better than the stories
told by Old Marathonians (as it were in the pub on Saturday
night). The stories were complicated by political issues.
Most old Marathonians belonged to one political party in
Athens and not that of the Old Salaminians (who also told
their stories in different pubs on the same Saturday night).
There may have been pro-Persian propaganda at work too.
It is not surprising that his story is tangled in its details and
that there appear to be serious gaps in it. Recent historians

disagree in the reconstructions of the events before and during the battle, but they all agree to disagree with Herodotus. Yet no historian in any age has ever doubted the broad outline of the account ; namely that a formidable Persian force landed in the Bay of Marathon in September 490 B.C., was decisively defeated by the Athenians (with the help, never to be forgotten, of the Platæans), that the Persian fleet then went home and no Persian force appeared on Greek soil till 10 years later. If that outline were seriously wrong ; had no Persians landed, had there been no battle, had the Persians won it, then subsequent history of the Eastern Mediterranean would not make sense. True we have not heard a Persian version, not even an official version. However, from our rich modern experience of official versions we can reconstruct it, and some day it may turn up, carved in stone. It would go something like this :—' After our glorious army disembarked at Marathon, the wretched Athenian levies of slaves and mercenaries attempted to attack, but were quickly put to flight with trifling loss on our side. We did not advance immediately to destroy Athens because the extreme scarcity of provisions in poverty-stricken and ill-governed Attica would have imposed undue hardship on our gallant troops, had they left their base of supplies. Moreover, the lateness of the season and unfavourable reports from our meteorological experts decided our Commander to linger no more on that exposed and inhospitable shore. . . But a bigger and better punitive expedition is now preparing to. . . . . ' In short, the Persian official version would make little difference.

Details about Marathon are not to be relied upon ; details about the campaigns of Alexander the Great are even worse. He was hardly cold in his grave before hostile political propaganda got to work on one side and deliberately concocted romantic fables on the other. The honest historian Arrian, writing more than four and a half centuries later did his best and did have Ptolemy's record before him, but the mess had already been made. Moreover Arrian had no knowledge of Asiatic geography beyond the Tigris and was confused by wild efforts of his predecessors to write Asiatic place names in Greek. Yet even if every detail about Alexander's expedition could be shown to be wrong, the general fact of his conquests has to be accepted ; again, because without it subsequent history would not make sense (cf. W. W. Tarn, *Alexander the Great*, 1948, Cambridge University Press).

A great deal of ancient history follows this kind of pattern. I would suggest that this apprehension of general trend and outline should be reckoned as folk-memory. When unrestrained by hostile criticism folk-memory shades off or grows into fable, but when the memory of some folk is checked by that of others it is not so insecure. Athenian folk-memory about the Persian Wars would not be exact in detail, but if Old Marathonians embroidered too much they would be checked by Old Salaminians. If both embroidered too much there was other Greek folk-memory at work down at Piraeus to check it and at other Greek ports oversea. There was also non-Greek Eastern Mediterranean folk-memory at work. Accounts get blurred after many generations, but not so very quickly nor always so very seriously. Sometimes the folk, Aristotle's ' many ', are more to be trusted than the ' learned ', specially those whose learning consists of ' -isms '. The learned of the 1880's were quite certain that there could never have been a Trojan War and there was no such citadel as Ilium on the map ; the whole story was fable, like the story of Persephone or Orpheus. Now their children or grandchildren stand confidently at the Skaian Gate and point to where exactly the Achaeans camped on the shore. Of course they may be right, assuming they know where shoreline was in 1200 B.C. and assuming that 1200 B.C. is the right date. They are quite sure which of the many ' topless towers of Ilium ' whose ruins are piled above each other were the ones attacked by Agamemnon. They are still a bit diffident about what the Trojan Horse may have been. That is a relief, because Herodotus was diffident and perhaps Homer too. And further, amid all this certainty, it is pleasant to reflect that Odysseus was too clever for all the rest of them. However, the point of all this digression is, that the learned have now begun to admit that there is something in folk-memory, and even occasionally quite a lot.

The difficulty with recent history may be the reverse of that of ancient history and more like the legal kind mentioned earlier. There is now no folk-memory and there are hardly any folk. There are newspapers but yesterday's paper goes to light today's fire and that is the end of it. Official records there are in quantities and of every conceivable kind. But could they produce a synoptic view even if they were all collated ; and can they be collated ?

Analogies from the more advanced sciences are unfavourable. Physicists used to assume that where there are several possible alternative hypotheses more evidence will sooner or later eliminate all except one, the ' true ' one. That was how it looked during the 18th and 19th centuries. It looks less like that now in the mid-20th. More evidence may kill off old hypotheses ; it may also breed new ones. There is no inherent reason in the nature of hypotheses or evidence why hypothetical birth rate should not exceed death rate or if death rate does exceed birth rate why all should not perish in the end. Why should one hypothesis survive, and if one, why not two ? Consider what is now happening to the physical ' cosmology ' of the astronomers. Much new evidence has been coming in during the past 20 or 30 years. Old hypotheses have been killed off, but not quite so fast as new ones are born. The time will come when the sources of information dry up ; because of the inherent imperfections of human instruments, because interstellar space is cloudy with dust and gas, because the earth's atmosphere is an imperfect medium for the transmission of radiation ; perhaps there are other obstacles too. The time may come when every visible object (' visible ' by radio waves as well as light waves) in the sky has been thoroughly examined by every possible method, only routine observations remain to be made and no new information is to be had. The time may come sooner or it may come later. When it does come, is it not likely that, since only some things have been examined, the cosmological theorists will find themselves with a good half-dozen alternative hypotheses on their hands and no way of deciding between them ? Is it at all likely that they will possess one triumphant ' true ' theory ? Would that not call for omniscience operating through infinite time with perfect instruments ?

Let us turn to more cheerful topics. I am contending that

M   [171]

there are basic techniques used by jurists and historians for obtaining factual evidence and for judging of its value. They are based on common practice and in common practice in the easy cases are used unconsciously. They are used consciously in the difficult cases with which lawyer and historian have to deal. They are not always equally successful but they are used. They are the proper technical basis for human sciences. They are not derived from physics. It would be nearer the mark to say that physics is derived from them, and that this has not been noticed because physics shirks all the difficult cases and thus can use a sort of nursery version of the techniques.

§5. At this point I must ask to be allowed what will appear at first to be a mere digression : a medical analogy or parable.

Digitalis is a useful drug for certain disorders of the heart (specially *auricular fibrillation*), but it is also a dangerous poison. The right dosage for one patient may kill another and have no appreciable effect upon a third. Patients differ according to the different states of their bodies and their minds. To use digitalis successfully it is first of all necessary to have standardized preparations, so that accurately measured doses can be administered. (The early disrepute of digitalis came from using crude and unstandardized material.) The treatment consists in giving first a carefully measured dose, of about the amount usually found effective and not dangerous, and then noting the effect on the pulse and heart sounds. After a definite interval a second dose is given, larger or smaller according to the effect of the first. Then when the effective safe dose has been found for that particular patient the treatment is continued quite regularly until the heart can function by itself, as discovered by giving diminishing doses.

The business of preparing, standardizing and administering digitalis calls for the theory and practice of physics and chemistry. Without these means the physician cannot proceed both effectively and safely. But these means alone are not enough. He must know also what he is trying to do, what his aim is. He is introducing a causal factor into a physical situation and he is doing something else, adjusting means to ends. Part of his specific medical theory consists in

[172]

understanding the ends for which he works, without which he would be trusting to chance, as much as if he failed to measure a dose of digitalis.

Medical practice has three primary ends : to alleviate pain, to save life (in an immediate emergency) and to restore health as completely as possible. These all refer to the patient, as a person, not as a thing. There is also a related but more technical end, to cure a particular disease, a more thing-like entity. This means that the physician has to put a stop to a specific disturbing process which may or may not cause pain, which may or may not immediately endanger life, and which always has some crippling or health destroying effect. Patients can, however, compensate to greater or less extent for the crippling effect of a chronic ailment, may appear healthy to the casual eye, and may sometimes even be stimulated to greater activity, for a time at least, by the compensatory effort. The sick genius is not entirely fabulous, but he seldom lasts long. To return to ends ; for the most part whatever ministers to any one end ministers also to the others. This is lucky because the minority of exceptional cases require difficult decisions, to abandon one or other of the ends. Some kinds of disease are reckoned to be incurable by all ordinary means and to kill in a short time. With such diseases the physician has to be content to alleviate pain so that the patient dies in peace ; at least he does so now. In the bad old days the physician seldom let him. Either on his own initiative or egged on by imploring relatives (' O doctor, can't you do something ! ') he tormented the dying up to the last.

In any case, nobody can do more than postpone death, and in treating the elderly the physician should take that into account. In treating the young he may well forget it and treat them as if they were immortal. Where a disease is not likely to be rapidly fatal but is crippling and painful, the physician should alleviate pain. This may by itself reduce the crippling effect. On the other hand it may not ; and he should avoid means of alleviation which increase the crippling or shorten life. Or so we assume. When the physician has to choose between harmless treatment which does not radically cure and dangerous treatment which may cure, he has a difficult and unenviable choice. As Plato said in the *Republic*, the physician should not set out to nurture permanent invalids. Nor yet should he violate the Hippocratic Oath by taking life instead of saving it. (Taking life is the lawyer's job.)

In adjusting means to ends the physician is dealing with persons and dealing with them one at a time ; he is not doing routine mechanical work. Engineers know that even in their profession there is such a process as ' nursing ' or ' humouring ' a machine to do more than can fairly be expected of it, and they find proper satisfaction in so doing. It is an end in itself, like writing a poem, and when it is applied to getting a cranky ship safe into harbour is useful and entirely laudable. Putting out to sea in a cranky ship can also be done, but is quite another story. Even the engineer is not free from the difficulties or the special fascinations of adjusting means to ends and deciding between incompatible ends.

The use of digitalis illustrates a method of experiment in medicine applied to a human subject. It will be seen that the experiment involves a relation between three terms, the drug, the disease and the individual patient. It is the first two that are attended to directly during the experiment, the third only indirectly, though the most important. It is about the patient that prediction is made, though in terms of the disease and the drug.

Another type of experiment in medicine is the testing of a suggested remedy for a human disease (practically always preceded by tests on comparable animal diseases). The method is to select a group of persons as varied as possible in all other respects, but all carefully diagnosed as suffering from that one disease, also selected for examination. The group, to be varied enough and statistically significant, should contain 100 or more persons. It should be divided into two similar and equal groups, the ' experimental ' and the ' control ' group ; but all members of both should appear to receive the same treatment so that nobody knows which group he is in. With a chronic disease, it may be helpful to switch over the two groups in the middle of the treatment, to note the effect of starting and stopping the treatment. After a sufficient length of treatment the results are examined with appropriate statistical analysis, to show amount and rate of recovery, and death rate, if any, in the two groups. Here we have experiment as genuine, complete, precise and all the rest of it, as in a physical laboratory ; but slow, difficult, expensive, often indecisive and quite spoiled if the members of the control group discover they are control, or if members of the experimental group are thrilled at getting the marvellous, new, infallible treatment.*

However, the main conclusion to be drawn is that this kind of experiment (and prediction) deals with relations between a remedy, a disease and a population. These are the entities studied, not individual persons at all. The whole procedure is designed to keep them out ; as, in contrast, the digitalis example is designed to put the individual in.

As disease has been mentioned, the question : What is health ? cannot be entirely avoided. There is no simple positive answer. There is a negative answer, though not simple nor complete. We can say that a healthy person does not have tuberculosis, diabetes, mumps, yellow fever, athlete's heart, jaundice, dropsy, etc. etc. This is valid as far as it goes, because these ailments can all be recognised as positive abnormal conditions, by specific types of pain and by physical signs. If you could make a complete list of diseases you could perhaps say : so and so has none of these ; there are no others ; therefore he is healthy. But there is no complete list. Moreover, even the few named are of very different types. The last two are names of symptoms only. The first four are taken to indicate causes and to name specific diseases. The other, athlete's heart, is of dubious status. Even among the specific diseases there are great differences. A man may have had mumps in the past and now be perfectly healthy. That cannot be said about diabetes and only with qualifications about tuberculosis.

Many abnormal symptoms can be expressed in quantitative terms and often the abnormalities are at the two extreme ends of a scale, with normal states intermediate. If so, there is

* The experiment works according to Mill's canons of induction ; it hardly needs the hypothetic-deductive method, though it is more satisfactory if definite ' hypotheses ' can be used. It is necessary to say this only because certain recent writers, thinking entirely in terms of advanced physical science, say there is no Millian induction at all. Compare, however, meteorology (§1 of this chapter).

often a wide range which is not abnormal and the exact mean position is no better than others to one side or the other. Again, that is to say that the abnormal may be more easily defined than the normal. Sometimes the normal is a maximum. The normal eye or ear has the maximum power of discrimination, but even this is not so very positive. It is like saying that a healthy mouth possesses the maximum number of teeth, which only means that none are missing.

These attempts do not get us far. Even if we did discover a complete absence of abnormalities or diseases, could we go on to claim perfect health? If we have no pains, do we have joy, happiness or even pleasure? The possession of health must depend in part upon absence of hindrances, but is that all? We do come across people who in spite of hindrances yet possess vigour, zest for life and are capable of harmonious activity; also others who suffer no visible hindrances and yet lack such positive qualities.

Suppose we abandon the search for individual health and consider the statistical collective approach. The longevity of a population is for many purposes a valid indication of its health. The fact that there is now a greater expectation of life in this country than there was 50 years ago, and much greater than 100 years ago, is taken to show that we are a healthier people. From the point of view of public authorities this is the reasonable and useful conclusion. Acts of Parliament and administrative action can and should be based on it. Yet this test is a bit negative after all. It means that over these 100 years, in this and other comparable countries the killing infections which once killed off many children and young adults now kill few or none. It may mean also, but does not necessarily mean, that the larger numbers of survivors are healthier than the smaller numbers of survivors of 100 years ago. Then quite a number of people lived to be 80, were never ill in their lives and also in full possession of their faculties, even their teeth, till they died of heart failure, cerebral hæmorrhage or something of the sort that is still beyond control. Many more now live to be 80, were never ill in their lives and die in the same way, though seldom with their teeth. That is a gain. But what about the large number of chronic invalids who can now be kept alive, and who have longevity without health ? That cannot be called a gain and no statistics at present compiled show how much it offsets the genuine gain. Nor do any statistics show how much of the time, money and professional skill in our hospitals is devoted to promoting health and how much to prolonging disease. It was a blot on older medical practice that they persecuted the dying and hastened their death with cruel and violent treatment ; is it not perhaps an equal blot on modern medical treatment that it indefinitely prolongs, though generally without pain, the process of dying ? Lastly, statistical health though useful for bureaucrats is not much help to medical men who try to cure sick persons always, and columns of figures never.

§6. The conclusion of the previous section, like the definition of health, is largely negative. Yet it may be the kind of conclusion with which we have to be content at the early stages of scientific endeavour. The worst error in the early stages is to expect to arrive at a complete view, to formulate a theory which is of universal application and is going to be the last word. The result is to take a very partial view, to formulate incoherent theories and fail to say even the first word. In any case, though the first word does belong to any proper science, the last one does not belong to science at all.

The next worse error is to expect the kind of success in human studies which the natural sciences have derived from opening up new realms of experience by new techniques. In human life we can expect only the more careful and systematic use of long familiar kinds of experience, the new consideration of old facts. If Freud and his ' unconscious ' are quoted to the contrary, the reply is that he has not shown us new facts but new ways of looking at old facts. The new ways are often useful, but so are the old ways. I have insisted on comparing psychology with meteorology for this reason as well as for others.

Suppose now we were in principle setting out to compile the *Statesman's Handbook*, as Aristotle did in fact. The first thing to notice is, as I have mentioned, that we operate under graver difficulties than he did, because collecting, collating and applying evidence is now a complex task calling for special techniques. In compensation we now see that this very process is part of our science. Also in compensation we have a very long historical perspective while he had a very short one. We ought now to be able to see that theory and practice must not be divorced, if only from experience of the errors that come from divorcing them and specially from misapplied analogies from misunderstood mathematics and physics.

Aristotle's *Handbook* was in one sense already out of date before he wrote, for the Greek city state was dying. That need not be a fatal defect. In the strictest sense every thing in every handbook that depends on historical events is out of date, and of necessity. It is for the statesman who interprets and applies the handbook to remedy the defect ; the handbook cannot interpret or apply itself.

Consider one aspect of Aristotle's discussion, one derived from Plato. The Greeks saw the central problem of politics to be how to reconcile order and freedom. Plato in founding his ideal Republic did suggest the prescription for the final solution that is not quite operative anywhere, but is laid up in Heaven. It is :—Select the right leaders, provide them with the right education, then leave them to act in the situation as they find it. No particular political problem can be solved before it crops up. But how are we to educate the rulers ? Plato, once he gets beyond his admirable kindergarten stage of Music and Gymnastics, does not help us. (We now know too much about pure mathematics and pure everything else.) Surprisingly, Aristotle does help us. His answer is simple. Given a working system of Law and Constitution, it will provide a practical education for both rulers and ruled, if only it is a mixed constitution that weights the scales fairly between different sections and interests. The process of education does not take place mainly in the Academy, or even Lyceum, but where Socrates was educated, in the dialectical process of public life. It is there that the ordinary citizens can voice their special views (however erroneous) and special complaints and the rulers obtain information and defend their policy. Without an effectively maintained Law and Constitution the dialectic does not work ; the rulers are ignorant of what is happening and so are the ruled. Both Plato and

[178]

Aristotle saw that the alternatives to good government are tyranny on the one side and anarchy on the other, and both strangely alike, for with them nobody knows what is happening. Aristotle also saw that Law and Constitution provide theory as well as practice. Perhaps he also saw that ' the price of liberty is eternal vigilance '.

In advocating a mixed Constitution Aristotle favours a system of checks and balances. He did not conceive these mechanically as the 18th century was liable to do, but rather as safeguarding public information and public discussion.

With his short historical perspective Aristotle saw these things sketchily and vaguely. He could not see what things were changing or how ; what things were permanent in spite of different appearances and different names given to them. Allowing for these limitations he said little, apart from some special matters, that later needed to be unsaid. That is as good a testimonial as any man of science can hope for.

§7. The human sciences of medicine, psychology, law, economics and politics predict human behaviour ; not very extensively or confidently perhaps, but they do it. The best practitioners do not ape the physicist in method nor do they use his special concepts, but each sticks to his own business. Prediction, however, is only a small part of the business of these disciplines, except for medicine. They are concerned first of all with facts (if I may call them so without causing confusion) rather than theories (if I may call them so without causing confusion). They must first record what has happened in its variety and complexity, with an eye to the concrete, not merely to the abstract. Social history must precede sociology, if there is ever to be anything worth the name.

Consider now a simple example of prediction, a matter of individual psychology at the commonsense level. Let us suppose some people are in a room where a committee is about to meet. The Secretary looks at his watch and says : ' Three minutes still before we begin. Smith is not here yet, but he will be. He said he would come and he is hardly ever more than two minutes early or one minute late. Brown, if he comes will be late and with a wonderful story about it, if we allow

[179]

him to tell it.' Here is prediction at work, springing from observation of the actual habits of the two men. They both have habits, but they are very different kinds of habit. Smith's habit of punctuality began by conscious effort even if it continues automatically without it. This is true whether he began the conscious efforts because his parents told him punctuality was a good thing and he obeyed without further reflection, or because he thought it all out for himself. If he thought it out, he may have done it on empirical lines, arguing that punctuality does in fact promote the greatest happiness of the greatest number ; or he may have deduced it from the moral law, or argued it in some other way. It makes no real difference. In any case he began to practise punctuality for a reason of some kind, either at first hand or second hand, though it was part reason, not complete, it was still reason. There is no need to enquire into any further ' cause ' of his behaviour. Moreover nobody needs to apologise for being punctual, or make excuses, or invent stories of how by a series of unexpected accidents he happened to arrive at the right time.

Brown's habit of unpunctuality may have begun by conscious effort in order to give him a chance of inventing ingenious stories ; but this is most unlikely. Even if it were true and did provide reason of a sort, it would be a very poor sort. It is the reason of the crank who thinks that thinking for yourself means thinking differently from everybody else. Brown's unpunctuality may be the result of ' causes ' which a close acquaintance with his life history might reveal ; it is unlikely to follow from a reason. Lastly, we can predict that if Brown is punctual on any occasion it will be by accident and that if Smith is unpunctual there will be a reason for it ; a special one which overrides his ordinary habit or ordinary reason.

Good habits are undoubtedly good, but as means not as ends. They can become divorced from their ends and cease to be good any more. We say that Smith's habit began as reason and continues as reasonable, we are thus putting Smith's behaviour as definitely on the right moral side. But consider his cousin Smythe. However well he may have started he has become a punctuality fiend ; he is always fussing about it and makes a nuisance of himself, letting what is really contrary to reason masquerade as rational.

Human behaviour operates at different levels and by different means, at different times and even at one and the same time. Habits, which are bits of the human machinery, can operate at different physiological levels, levels of complexity. These physiological differences of level should not be confused with those of moral level in terms of good and evil. The good and rational at the highest level may use the machinery of habit at any level. So also may the evil and contra-rational. Christian moralists have always recognized that ' spiritual ' evil is worse than mere ' carnal ' evil.

All that has been said in this section is old-fashioned simple-minded stuff, quite out of touch with all the ' -isms ' of the last two centuries and the technical jargon that goes with them. Yet it does keep clear of the fallacy they have in common. However much they contradict one another in other respects they are concocted by ' superior persons ' who despise all the rest. I must conclude with something even more old-fashioned, using to begin with the previous illustration of punctuality.

We could say, according to one type of ' -isms ', that the sole difference between Smith and Brown is that Smith happens to like punctuality, just as he happens to like eating oysters, while Brown happens to dislike the one as he also does the other. Smith and Brown have these purely private fads or fancies and that is all that can be said ; praise or blame are quite out of place, except as somebody else's private fad or fancy. This attitude ignores one conspicuous difference between the two kinds of fancy. Eating oysters or refraining from eating them has no obvious public consequences, whereas punctuality and its opposite have, and these consequences are of the special types that are praised or blamed. We do not give moral praise to one man for being big and strong, nor blame to another for being small and weak, though these differences have public consequences. Even the people who expound this kind of theory do not apply it to their own behaviour, which they believe to have public consequences and which they believe to be praiseworthy.

There are two other theories of the ' Nothing-but ' type

which are rather more plausible ; the theory of pure selfish prudence and the theory of pure social conformity. Neither of these is a theory of reason in action because neither is universal. The one makes each individual his own separate centre ; the other makes each separate society the centre for the individuals who happen to belong to it. The one says that Smith is punctual because on the whole he gets more private pleasure from punctual than from unpunctual behaviour. The second that he is punctual because he thereby obtains the approval of the group to which he belongs. There is no doubt that both these factors are at work, but sometimes they are opposed, sometimes they operate on the same side. They obviously are not the sole factors, except possibly at very low levels of intelligence. Theories that one of them is the sole factor could not be put forward except by learned men nourished on ' isms ' which they never apply to themselves.

Both these theories ignore the facts, which are more complex than they can admit. In the first place punctuality is a modern virtue, unknown before the existence of mechanical clocks and watches. Even in societies where it is widely practised there are many who, like Brown, are never punctual, and many more who are seldom punctual ; but blame goes no further than treating them as tiresome and rather stupid. There are very few who are like Brown in taking pleasure in unpunctuality. Most of the unpunctual would go no further than to say that it is less trouble. Again, few of the punctual get much pleasure out of it ; and when all the rest are unpunctual they get none. They do take pride in it, often too much ; but that is not the same as pleasure. In unpunctual societies the few who are punctual are not blamed or objected to ; they are more probably faintly admired and praised in a joking fashion. Lastly, for all the differences in behaviour of different individuals and different societies, we do all make some judgments that claim to be general and not purely individual preferences or mere reflections of behaviour habits in our own surroundings. Nor do we make them as outsiders and spectators only, but as participators and yet as reasonable and in that sense objective. Even if these claims do not produce unanimity, that does not render them all entirely false and worthless. It indicates that our reasons (plural) are not the whole complete Reason, not that they are quite unreasonable.

Another theory which cannot be accepted, but has some sense in it, is the theory that morally good action has ' survival value ' and morally bad action the reverse, and that the survival value constitutes the criterion. The basic objection here is that in most cases we do not know the survival value of different types of action and cannot know it till we are all dead. In some cases at least we know it and dismiss it as irrelevant. When a man loses his life in trying to rescue someone from danger and loses it in vain, his act has no survival value but we do not think the worse of him for that. It can be argued, and indeed has been, that the practice of the blood feud and of tribal warfare has survival value, at least for those few families and tribes that do in fact survive, because of the discipline and mental and physical alertness that the practice engenders. Yet none of those who do argue this deliberately remove themselves and their families from the enervating surroundings of civilized communities, where homicide is held to be a crime, to enjoy the bracing air of blood feud and tribal warfare. In short, the survival value theory has the defects of the old ' *Fable of the Bees, or Private Vices Public Benefits* ' (Bernard Mandeville, 1714, Ed. F. B. Kaye, Oxford University Press, 1924).

For all that, the notion of social utility must be taken seriously. Human actions are not good in themselves unless they are the kind of actions which in general have public consequences and these consequences can in general be approved as morally good. Let us grant the Kantian view that a moral agent is autonomous and therefore can act in accordance with and for the sake of the moral law ; that the criterion for judging of that accord is that the rule for the act is universal, and equally obligatory on any agent in a similar position relative to other agents ; that the act is a way of treating other moral agents as ends in themselves, not as mere means ; that it is also a way of entering into and living in a realm of ends. Granted all this, we cannot apply any Kantian criterion to acts that have no public consequences. That an act produces consequences of which we approve is *a* reason and a necessary one for our approving of the act ; but it is not the sole reason and it is not one which the agent himself can always use. The agent can use external or Utilitarian criteria only when his act is of a routine sort and therefore not very important morally for him. A too exclusively Kantian view leaves the moral agent in a vacuum ; a too exclusively Utilitarian view leaves out the moral agent.*

Let us return to the rather trivial example of punctuality, useful because it is rather trivial yet can mean more than appears at first sight and also because we know its history. The virtue of punctuality was invented in Western Europe, the only virtue that was invented there ; all the rest have come from farther East. It is also the first and best product of the Technological Revolution.† It was due originally to the Rule of the Benedictine Order, but could not become prominent in ordinary life until pocket watches as well as public clocks became common in the 17th century. King Louis XIV is the modern prototype of the Punctual Man, and should receive credit for that, if for nothing else. If he is quoted correctly, he put the matter in its proper light, saying, ' Punctuality is the politeness of Princes.' As everybody else has to wait for the Prince he can and should show his respect for his fellow men by arriving precisely at the time appointed.

Politeness is the starting point of the social virtues and is always a large part of them, provided it expresses sincere respects for others. It easily degenerates to hypocrisy and also to etiquette, to complicated silly rules. Still, even if King Louis sank deep in hypocrisy, pedantry and silliness, and his ministers and courtiers too, his punctuality in dispatch of business and ceremonial remained of public use and benefit. Whatever his private state of mind the King who started it was showing his respect for his subjects, openly, publicly, as a sacramental act, in the sight of God.

What Louis XIV did in a small way, but very conspicuously,

---

* It is noticeable that Kant when challenged on special points, e.g. that it is never permissible to tell a lie, used Utilitarian arguments. This was not necessarily an inconsistency.

† In spite of the early date of the mechanical clock (13th century if not earlier), I think ' technology ' is the right term. But for the astronomical science of the Greeks there would have been no standard Solar or Sidereal Day, nor uniform division of the day against which to standardize mechanical clocks.

St. Benedict had done earlier in a much larger way. The truly other-worldly man who plans and acts solely for the greater glory of God, can also be much more practical and down to earth than the purely secular man. He knows that he must cut his coat according to his cloth, and that no magic, pseudo-science or wishful thinking will make a coat for him out of nothing. St. Benedict arranged for his monks to say their prayers punctually, but also and necessarily to do their work, eat their meals and take their rest punctually. Thus they did better work, their meals were better cooked and more whole-some, and they slept better, lived longer and healthier lives. ' All these things were added unto them.' Even if it all fell to the level of habit, or lower, the sacramental nature of the initiating impulse was temporarily corrupted not destroyed, without it there would have been nothing to corrupt.

This sketchy introduction to a subject which goes beyond the scope of the present book may well be concluded by quoting something written rather more than two centuries ago, in an age when secularist theories and the secular attitude were just as fashionable as now. ' Whatever the world thinks, he who hath not much meditated upon God, the human mind, and the *summum bonum*, may possibly make a thriving earth-worm, but will most indubitably make a sorry patriot and a sorry statesman.' (Berkeley, *Siris*, §350.)

CHAPTER X

COSMOLOGIES

Theology and cosmology · Four cosmological antinomies · Politics and cosmology

§1. ALREADY I have said or hinted too much about cosmology to be able to avoid saying more. The positivist programme of adhering to separate and distinct items of information and never attempting to relate them to the whole to which they belong is plausible at first sight in the realm of physics, less so in biology, impossible in human studies. In any case no positivist has ever carried out his own programme. Each has his own kind of cosmology, even theology, mainly negative, but not the less *a priori*, dogmatic or metaphysical for that, nor more consistent.

It is simplest to begin by stating my own convictions. I cannot believe in a cosmos without God, for if the universe is well ordered, at all, anywhere, I did not make it so, nor did you. To say it made itself by chance is to say nothing. Consequently cosmology for me must begin with God and end with God. In other words, I cannot dismiss as superstitious fools, Plato, Aristotle, Descartes, Locke, Spinoza, Leibniz and Kant, as I did dismiss in the previous chapter, Comte, Marx and Spencer. Apart from their greater intelligence the seven first mentioned are in better agreement on fundamentals than the three latter. A cosmology which excludes Nature is slightly less absurd than an atheistic one, because Nature cannot be the beginning nor the end. For a man to construct a cosmology which excludes all other men may not seem absurd to him, but it does to the rest of us. Therefore I start with a threefold scheme : God, Man, Nature ; and could, if pressed, defend it by Occam's razor as the most economical.

Apart from this first accusation against positivists, there is another, on moral grounds. Positivism leaves the door wide open to the ' Technicians' Illusion ', a dangerous one. Positivists themselves are armchair critics, who do no work and therefore very little harm. Technicians on the other hand do

[186]

work and may do a great deal of harm. They may concoct cosmologies out of some technique and, if they listen to positivists, mistake it for science and guaranteed truth.

The technicians' chief illusions are two, and were pointed out by Socrates. The first is that because a man can do some things successfully he can do many other different things equally successfully ; in fact almost anything. The second is that practising any technique is an inherently virtuous act, whatever the consequences. Turning technicians into technologists does not diminish the illusions ; it makes them more dangerous, because more powerful. Turning technicians into scientific theorists makes the second illusion relatively harmless, but enhances the first till it may become universal theory, cosmology, metaphysics or theology ; namely the belief that through some special technique the nature of the universe is revealed to the practitioner. (Cf. Chapter V, §3.)

Cosmology begins with an attitude or basic choice which determines how in general a man reacts to his environment, to the world which confronts him. There is a saying attributed to the late Professor A. A. Bowman, that one large part of mankind treat life as something to be exploited, another large part as something to be despaired of, and only a small third part as something to be redeemed. The last attitude is the basis of Bowman's own philosophy (see *A Sacramental Universe*, 1939, Princeton University Press, specially *Introduction*, pp. 1-13).

Here are three basic attitudes determining three types of cosmology. The first springs from pride, greed or fear, the second from the more sophisticated attitude of self-pity.* Both of these are attitudes of rejection ; the first dangerous, idolatrous or atheistic. The second is not itself dangerous, though it may turn to the first it can also be a step towards the genuinely religious attitude. This is the third, an attitude of acceptance and of faith, hope and charity.† The terms ' attitude ' and ' choice ' are intended to emphasize that action

---

* For the close alliance of self-righteousness and self-pity see the speeches of Milton's Satan and the late Adolph Hitler. Many other modern secularists might be quoted too.

† St. Paul's πίστις should perhaps be translated ' sincerity ' as well as ' faith ' ; his ἐλπίς as ' sanity ' as well as ' hope ' ; for his ἀγάπη there is no English equivalent.

comes first and thought second, will before intellect ; or perhaps together, but not the other way round. For all that, an attitude or choice need not be irrational, as some suppose ; only it belongs to Practical Reason, in Kantian terms, not to Theoretical Understanding. Choice is rational if it is seen as specific and according to universal rule ; but it has to be seen, i.e. formulated, and we usually find that by then we have already chosen.

I propose to take an unfashionable line, to use the notorious Ontological Argument for the existence of God, and try to rescue it from the narrow and pedantic treatment from which it has suffered. I shall begin, roughly, where Kant left off. He defined three types of argument—Ontological, Cosmo-logical, Teleological. The last two are hypothetical ; ' If God exists then . . . . . ', so cannot stand without the first, which is categorical. I should prefer to say that there is one argument only which must first be put categorically and then amplified by filling in what would otherwise be bare assertion of existence without explanation as to how and to what end. The ontological argument is not to be taken as a syllogism or anything like one, since it would draw an existential conclusion from non-existential premises, therefore be invalid. It is, as the first syllable of the name says, an appeal to, or rather through, experience ; experience in general more than in particular, the whole of experience, not one part excluding other parts. It is wrong to claim that God is here and therefore not there, now and not then, as has to be done when we claim that any *object* exists or any *event* occurs. Moreover, any statement we make about the character of a particular object or event is based upon imagination * as well as actual experi-ence, and again imagination is exclusive as well as inclusive. Mr. Brown is in this place, not that, where Mr. Smith is. We can be sure of that because the two men are unlike in some respects though like in others ; and without imagination we could not arrive at this assurance. Conceiving comes in in addition to sense and imagination to keep us from contradict-ing ourselves or breaking other proper cognitive rules. I could

* ' Imagination ' is here used in the 18th century sense of constructing or reconstructing possible experiences by means of sensory images ; the imagination of the engineer.

[188]

imagine Mr. Brown as both tall and short, old and young, or as identical with Mr. Smith, if I forgot to imagine consistently.

I do not and cannot imagine God. I can and perhaps do imagine idols. I can and do imagine the Devil ; possibly wrongly and inconsistently, for the Devil raises difficult problems that cannot be discussed at the moment. Setting imagination aside, I can conceive experience in general as being of a certain kind and not of an opposed kind. Certain special experiences may appear as specially exemplary while others may appear less so, but I must not take any exclusively. Then I can conceive of a universal Being whom I cannot perceive or imagine, firstly and inadequately as the Power behind experience or the Cause producing it, and secondly, less inadequately, as Intelligence and Will ; in short ' the Being whom men commonly call God and worship '. By means of my conceiving, for I have no other means, I come into His presence. To specify the character of the conception I am referring to is the (very lengthy) business of the Cosmological and Teleological aspects of the argument, which should cover all modes of activity, experience and cognition.

Let me put the matter another way ; I may see somebody whom I recognise as a friend and then talk with him. It is the mutual conversation that confirms, what sight merely suggested that he is a friend, not a stranger, nor a lifeless physical object, nor a hallucination. But my friend is a physical object and so am I. Our conversation is carried on by certain special physical means, and not easily if at all without them. I can speak with God at any time in any place by any means in the course of any activity. If I frequently do not do so the obstacle is on my side. I can speak *of* another man in that man's absence when I cannot speak *to* him. Nobody can speak *of* God without speaking *to* God. For those to whom God is absent there is nothing to speak *of*. This is to put the ontological argument negatively. To put it positively in one sentence ; the presence of God is the answer to prayer.

The use of the ontological argument is to purge the mind of idolatry. It has no compulsive force. If it is accepted it is accepted freely ; if it is rejected it is rejected freely. This is true of all arguments, for all are dialogues in which nobody

[189]

can be compelled to take part against his will, not even the man who argues with himself.* The most persuasive of arguments for the existence of God is just the behaviour of those few who act sincerely as in God's presence. The most convinced anti-Christian is the one who as a child has been talked to about Christ by those who manifestly behaved as though Christ did not exist.

Many, perhaps most people, cherish distorted faiths and conceptions, idols, which stand in the place of God ; creatures usurping the place of the Creator. Idolatry at its lowest is the worship of power, wealth, pleasures, or just self ; but, short of suicide, everybody trusts, seeks or worships something. It is always possible on this occasion or that to ignore God, to act as though God did not exist ; it is only too easy. I do not believe it is possible to do so always. God is never entirely without witnesses, the saints, though they are lamentably few. At the other end of the scale, the wrongdoers, who are plentiful enough, are apt to be brought unwillingly into the presence of God in their wrongdoing or afterwards. Again, it is always possible on this occasion or that to suspend judgment, to be completely agnostic ; but it is not possible always or systematically. Or, if it is possible, it is to universalize the attitude of ' I couldn't care less.' To do that is inhuman ; it might be called brutish if that were not a libel on the brutes.

I must explain why I have not stressed the illumination or ecstasy of the mystic. It is because it is rare, of various grades and types, and spurious imitations are commoner than the real thing. The value of such experience depends upon what leads up to it and what comes from it. The aspect of religious experience that needs to be stressed is that of choice, decision, commitment, which leads to action, to good or evil. In case any one has difficulty in seeing where God comes in in matters of choice, I can only add what Hooker says : ' In doing evil we prefer a less good before a greater, the goodness whereof is by reason investigable and may be known.' (*Ecclesiastical Polity*, I, 7, 7.)

* Many people still seem to assume that all arguments ought to be like mathematical demonstrations and that these are compulsive. Nobody can be compelled to accept the premises of a mathematical demonstration however flawless the argument.

If it be granted that cosmology begins with choice, and when made explicit is expressed as theology, it still remains to inquire what attitude towards the physical world follows. Even a pan-psychic cosmology is still an attitude towards the physical world, though negative and, as I believe, distorted. So also is a pantheistic cosmology, and seriously distorted because it confuses the Creator with His creatures. We should distinguish and we should take the physical world seriously— ' the Earth is the Lord's and the fullness thereof '.

If this also be granted then we must start further philosophizing by asserting the duality of the Universe ; there is a Spiritual or Mental realm and a Physical or Material. The common threefold division, Nature, Man and God admits this and indicates that Man is an intermediary : the Great Amphibian, sharing both realms. Common sense has never had any qualms about duality ; many metaphysicians have (here we must include positivists as metaphysicians of the deepest dye). They have seen some philosophers exaggerate duality and so lapse into dualism and difficulties ; Descartes is the outstanding example. Seeing this they have shrunk into a negative monism, spiritualist or materialist. As Bowman pointed out the only result of such monism when systematically worked out is to introduce surreptitiously some new kind of dualism, worse than that of Descartes, who at least draws a distinction that can be used.*

Any honest dualism such as that of Plato, Descartes or Kant is better than surreptitious dualism. These three drew their distinction in a different way, on different grounds and the other two gave more to the non-spiritual realm than did Descartes, perhaps too much. Possibly Descartes gave too little, but what he said is easily understood—one realm is what physical science studies, the other is what we discover by reflection on our own activities. The difficulty that appears immediately is that the two kinds of study are not quite so neatly separable. If the second is taken to mean ' introspection ' it is a process which by itself leads nowhere. If the study of physics

---

* A. A. Bowman, *A Sacramental Universe*, Chapters II to IV. I realise now that my attempt to avoid duality on Whiteheadean lines in *The Natural History of Mind*, 1936, was no more than ' Prolegomena to Kantian Dualism '.

is taken quite strictly as chrono-topographical and nothing else it leads too short a way. However, this is not the place to pursue these awkward questions further, beyond saying that serious trouble arises only when the distinction is misapplied to make a complete separation.

Scientific investigation goes most smoothly and easily when nobody inquires into fundamentals ; so far the positivists are right. As soon as somebody begins to inquire, then cosmology impinges on science and trouble begins too. It is seen that fundamentals look paradoxical, and whatever statement is made somebody else produces an antithetical statement ; but that looks equally paradoxical. It is convenient to take up the discussion in terms of Kant's Antinomies. Not that his discussion is satisfactory ; rather that it is not, but for reasons outside his control, namely the peculiar dogmatic state of scientific knowledge in his day. In the late 18th century it still looked as though Newton had spoken the last word (and Euclid too). Nobody could possibly foresee the great empirical and theoretical discoveries of the 19th century, though they were just below the horizon—the year 1800 is almost precisely the turning point, when John Dalton began work on the chemical atomic theory and Thomas Young on the wave theory of light, the first of the new constellations. Worse still, in Kant's day it looked as though there was no escape from the rigid determinism of Laplace and his universal Calculator ; i.e. that in principle all positions and paths of all material particles could be calculated forward to the remotest future and back to the remotest past. This is now seen to be only a nightmare, since it is based upon a number of false assumptions.*

§2. It would take a long time to discuss Kant's Four Antinomies adequately ; brief comments must suffice. His statements are as set out below :—

I. THESIS : the world has a beginning in time, and is enclosed within limits of space.

---

* Cf. Karl Heim, *The Transformation of the Scientific World View*, trans. A. W. Whitehouse, 1953, SCM Press. A number of theoretical physicists have said much the same, e.g. cf. von Weizsäker, *The History of Nature*, 1951.

ANTITHESIS : the world has no beginning in time, and no limits in space, but is infinite as regards both time and space.

II. THESIS : every composite substance in the world is made up of simple parts, and nothing whatever exists but the simple, or that which is composed of the simple.

ANTITHESIS : no composite thing in the world is made up of simple parts, nor does anything simple exist anywhere in the world.

III. THESIS : causality in conformity with laws of nature is not the only causality, from which all the phenomena of the world can be derived. To explain those phenomena it is necessary to suppose that there is also a free causality.

ANTITHESIS : there is no freedom, but all that comes to be in the world takes place entirely in accordance with laws of nature.

IV. THESIS : there exists an absolutely necessary being, which belongs to the world either as a part or the cause of it.

ANTITHESIS : there nowhere exists an absolutely necessary being, either in the world, or outside of the world as its cause.

The Antithesis in each case stands for ordinary everyday procedure and commonsense notions ; the positivist view as Comte (not Kant) called it. The assertion that is implied is a reasonable empirical generalization ; the denial that is made explicit is different. For instance, it is true that all portions of space known to us in experience are related to other bits outside them. That this process of successive external relations *has no end* is not given in experience. It is dogmatic *a priori* metaphysics based on imaginative construction. Its character is slightly concealed from view by its vagueness.

The Thesis in each case is openly dogmatic, *a priori* and metaphysical ; it is speculative and risky ; it contains something which common sense never thinks about and dislikes when suggested to it.

It is tempting to treat these disputes as purely verbal, but succumbing to the temptation does not put an end to them. They are conveniently set out, as Kant sets them, in pairs of opposites ; but that is a concession to a human foible in favour of dilemmas and dialectic, and against trilemmas and trialectic —if I may be pardoned such solecisms.

It is easiest to start with the 2nd Antinomy. Ostensibly

this states the debate between the Atomic Theory and its rival, conveniently called the Plenum Theory for it denies the empty space which the Thesis requires. Up to Kant's day the discussion still had no bearing on physical science because nobody before Dalton and Young had successfully used techniques for dividing things. When that had been done it was discovered that if you did your dividing one way you came to an end with indivisibles ; and if you did your dividing another way you did not, but found you were dealing with a continuum. Thesis and Antithesis are complementary not contradictory. This is a matter of technical operations, which had not yet been performed in the 18th century. Discussion in Kant's day turned on something else, namely the Newtonian or absolute theory of space, in which atomic theory is most naturally formulated, *versus* Leibnizian or relational theory, in which Plenum theory is most naturally formulated.*

Newtonian space leads to difficulties but is the theory in terms of which everybody thinks (including Leibniz and his followers) for ordinary purposes, until the difficulties crop up when all turn over for the time being to Leibnizian terms. The trouble had already loomed up in Zeno's paradoxes. Achilles and the Tortoise provide a puzzle as long as we state the case ambiguously, combining discontinuous units and Newtonian absolutes with continuity and Leibnizian relations. If you forget all this and are content with a single technical question and apply the appropriate technique of calculation you get a plain answer, which tells you when and where Achilles overtakes the Tortoise. You can use another technique suitable for answering other questions but then you must not expect a clear answer to that first question. Quite apart from any calculations there is still a problem, not mathematical, nor technical, but general, metaphysical and cosmological, and not I believe very important, though intriguing. Therefore in every generation one set of philosophers disinter Zeno and another set bury him again.

The 1st Antinomy tells a rather different story ; technique comes in in a different way and complementarity not at all.

* Newtonian space can be treated in terms of continuity and Leibnizian in terms of discontinuity, but the reverse is easier.

Kant states definitely the general physical problems. Increased factual information has had a direct bearing though not a conclusive one ; it has opened up the new possibilities much more than it has closed them. It has, however, decisively changed our views about time. Had all events been strictly reversible as the Laplacean Calculator assumes, then infinite temporal duration would have to be assumed, as many Greeks did assume ; beginning or ending in time would be incomprehensible. Given that there are some irreversible events then the Thesis, asserting finite time, is no longer absurd even if not established.

However, let us start with space, which is not so difficult. The number of bodies of all sorts which have been observed, though very large indeed is still finite and the volume they occupy finite too ; because a finite number of observers have worked for a finite time using a finite number of instruments of finite range and resolving power. As more observations are recorded the numbers get larger but no power on earth will make them infinite. This can be said equally well at any stage in the history of science, and was said, in effect, by Archimedes. On the other hand nobody can yet claim that all bodies that are in principle observable have been observed or that they must be within the region of space to which observation has so far been confined. At present that claim is groundless, so that the antithesis is not refuted. Even if the time comes when that claim can be made, the Thesis will not be thereby established. So much for space—for the time being.

Time is not like space in one respect at least. We examine bodies near us in detail and we assume that more distant bodies we can examine only in less detail are similar, on the grounds that a body is indifferent to mere position in space ; whether it is here or there. Nothing has yet cropped up to throw doubt on this assumption about spatial indifference. (See Appendix.) We cannot make a corresponding kind of assumption about time. We have no clear evidence of any completely reversible temporal processes and plenty of irreversible processes.* The near past resembles the present

* Of all ancient Greek theories the least tenable would appear to be that of *isonomia* ; that all process is not only reversible but actually reversed.

in some respects, and presumably the near future will resemble the present in some respects. The longer the time span considered, the weaker the analogical argument becomes. The one thing we can be sure about the long run is that it differs from the short run, in part at least, perhaps entirely. The idea of a world in which everything was constant, cyclic or reversible, in which events could go equally backwards or forwards (as Plato imagined in the fable in his *Statesman*) would be a nightmare.

Nevertheless we can have no empirical information about the past except so far as it was in some way like the present. Therefore we can have no information about an absolute beginning, much less an absolute end. Neither can we have information about endlessness. Speculation is free either way. We can say that modern astronomy and geology show that things have been going on for a very long time and may go on much longer too. They do not show when they began or if they ever did begin. At the back of speculation on these matters there is the divergence between Newtonian and Leibnizian types of space-time theory. Given a Newtonian view there is no difficulty about infinity of space ; in a completely empty container without boundaries there is ' room ' for anything. On a Leibnizian view there is every difficulty, for space is a relation between things not inherently spatial, and where there are no ' things ' there is no space. There is a similar divergence between two possible views of time. We may perhaps conclude that the primary puzzle of the 1st Antinomy is like that of the 2nd.

These two Antinomies cannot be dismissed as just erroneous formulations, the result of mistaking complementarity for contradiction. Where complementarity comes in, in the 2nd, it is technical and cosmologically irrelevant. Space-time theory does seem to present a genuine antinomy, a puzzle without a solution ; but one that is purely intellectual. Or, rather, one that is extra-intellectual ; something that the intellect does not compass and perhaps cannot compass. However the puzzle does not alter our practice in any way, neither in ordinary life nor scientific investigation. We apprehend and use any piece of information in the same way whether we are Newtonians or Leibnizians, or dodge erratically from one to the other, or even find some masterly compromise, such as Kant attempted. Thus these two antinomies can at least be passed over lightly.

It is true, however, that actual empirical information does alter our world outlook, more information has widened it and deepened our perspective. The natural sciences have revealed the incredibly remote, large, small and various. What is most revealing about all these revelations is the way that they have been made from one obscure source by one obscure kind of creature in the middle sized realm, neither large nor small. That is staggering. There is nothing staggering about large numbers except that men can discover them and use them. It is worth remembering that not all these discoveries date from the 20th century. Archimedes had some idea of the vastness of the physical world, Greek poets commented on it, and Boethius was quite definite about it (cf. *Consolatio* Bk. II, c. 7). Even the most hidebound ecclesiastic never seems to have smelt heresy in Boethius, a most popular author throughout the Middle Ages.

§3. The 3rd and 4th Antinomies tell a different story ; they are concerned with problems which affect conduct, are reflections of conduct, and are cosmologically and theologically relevant. The progress of science since Kant's day has also altered the atmosphere of discussion and widened our outlook ; again by opening up possibilities more than by closing them. These Antinomies call for discussion of the concepts of cause (two senses), of chance and of irreversibility.

If we take ' cause ' in the Humean sense or that of Kant himself as discussed in the *Analytic* of his first *Critique*, then the statements of the Antitheses are unexceptionable from the point of view of physics. All causes as discovered are inter-mediary or linking processes, so that there cannot be a first or last or extra cause of that kind. Those causes we discover are contingent in the sense that the one we find operating *here* might equally well have operated *there* instead, while another one operated *here*. There would be nothing more to say if the physical sciences never revealed anything except links in reversible processes and if they always revealed them everywhere ; as Hume and his followers seem to assume. In that case the two theses would be entirely arbitrary assumptions without any kind of empirical backing, as many determinists and secularists have said (cf. Karl Heim *The Transformation of the Scientific World View*).

The most important change since Kant has been the study of thermodynamics. This began as a branch of engineering, the theory of the steam engine, but has become a theory of cosmic significance, though for that purpose it needs to be interpreted cautiously. The most important aspect of it is the 2nd Law of Thermodynamics. That events of type B occur after those of type A and never before is not to be dismissed as contingent but is necessary under conditions in a special sense of ' necessary '. And these conditions are *given to* us in experience and not, like Kant's *a priori* imposed *by us*, on experience. For example, things that are uphill tend to fall down hill when left to themselves, and never, never to fall uphill when left to themselves. However, not all things on hillsides or elsewhere are always or of necessity left to themselves ; they may be blown by the wind or carried by animals. Interference from outside does not cheat the 2nd Law, because the Law describes a tendency that can take different routes under different conditions, not one fixed route.

The next and closely related point is that chance has to be admitted to what I am tempted to call ' honorary status ' as a kind of causal factor.* By giving room to both chance and causal determination of the traditional sort physics now also gives room for choice. We can go back to Aristotle who said that events may occur by necessity, by chance or by choice or by a combination of these. The change has not been brought about by Heisenberg's Uncertainty Principle (a minor matter applying only to the sub-atomic realm) but by 19th century kinetic theory of gases, thermodynamics and extended use of statistical theory and probability. Recent ideas were pretty completely anticipated by C. S. Peirce in 1892

---

* If I may be allowed such expressions, ' chance ' is still an expression of human ignorance or impotence, but necessary ignorance or impotence, not just casual.

(*The Doctrine of Necessity Examined*, reprinted in *The Philosophy of Peirce*, Ed. J. Buchler, 1940). The Laplacean Calculator is competent to deal with the Solar System, and welcome, but not with other things. Although writing before Laplace launched his Calculator, Kant was already haunted by him and had to exercise great ingenuity to find room for human freedom in a totally predetermined world. Incalculable, even undetermined, events can now be accepted as scientifically respectable. That in itself is not enough, or it is too much. A totally random universe would exclude freedom more effectively than a totally determined one ; even the loophole of Kant or Spinoza would be closed. Freedom or choice as we know it calls for an environment which is partly determined, therefore controllable or determinable in principle, but partly undetermined, so giving ' room ' or ' play ' for intervention. Controlling intervention can be exercised by an organism with instinctive grasp or rudiment-knowledge of which events are which, if the organism has instruments (e.g. at a high level, sense organs, brain and limbs) to control or direct the otherwise uncontrolled or undirected. Human technical achievement shows in detail how this happens. The technician describing what he proposes to do must put his verbs in the future tense and active voice—the language of freedom. The pure physicist in dealing with evidence uses, as he must, the past tense and the passive voice—the language of determination. From this necessity springs the old illusion, embodied already in folklore, of determin*ism* ; the -ism alone is illusory.

After these preliminaries let me state more definitely and then exemplify the first two laws of thermodynamics ; they are best put simply as Postulates of Impotence (Sir Edmund Whittaker, *Proc. Roy. Soc. Edin.* October 1941).

The 1st Law is that it is impossible to extract from any machine more energy than is put in ; energy balance-sheets balance exactly on the scale of magnitude of human operations. The 2nd is that it is impossible to obtain useful work on the human scale by transferring heat from a colder place to a hotter. Transfer of heat from a hotter to a colder place goes on spontaneously, and where it is happening useful work can be obtained (e.g. in a steam engine). The qualifying clause

' on the human scale ' is needed because the 2nd Law is the large scale collective result of a very large number of very small random events. On a very small scale and for a very short time there may be fluctuations in the reverse direction, from colder to hotter as well as from hotter to colder; but not on the large scale nor for any length of time. All heat energy tends to become uniformly distributed and useless, and all other forms of energy tend to degrade to heat energy.

Where there is a stream tumbling down a hillside, the initial gravitational potential energy of the water higher up is being degraded or running to waste in warming up the water and the bed of the stream to a small extent. How much warmer at any stage varies with actual conditions, but at no stage can the water or things in contact with it become colder. At the end when the water has reached the lowest possible level, the sea, all the gravitational potential energy of the water has been dissipated, and so has the kinetic energy of moving water *en route*. That is, unless something has interfered, e.g. a human device producing useful work. If that has interfered the 2nd Law has not been cheated, though for the time being a little less energy has been degraded to uniformly distributed heat energy. Energy is always being degraded but not always by the same amount nor always in the same place.

Suppose I have a house nearby and fit a hydraulic ram in the stream to pump water from it to a cistern in the roof. Then a fraction of the water running through the ram goes up to the cistern and gains gravitational potential energy. The rest of the water passes down as before, still warmed up but a trifle less warmed up than before. Later on all the water in the cistern passes down through the house pipes into the drains and finally to the sea with the rest. In the end all the gravitational potential of that lot of water too is degraded, and things are exactly as before the ram was fitted—except that we who occupy the house have drunk the water, cooked with it and washed with it. This explains what is meant by ' useful work ' and is a simple model of all the processes by which life is maintained on the surface of this earth.

Consider now another example, this time the essential or fundamental life process. When the sun shines on bare earth

[200]

the energy of radiation all runs to waste in warming up soil and air. As soon as green plants begin to grow there, useful work is being done building up the plant tissues, which possess high chemical potential energy, from substances of low chemical potential ; water, carbon dioxide and dissolved salts. Again the 2nd Law is not cheated, the plants have done what the hydraulic ram does, only far more skilfully than any man-made machine. Air and soil are still warmer from the sun's radiation, but not quite so much as before the plants began to grow. Green plants only grow, as hydraulic rams only work, where there is a ' stream' of energy running to waste ; that is at the sunlit surface of seas, rivers, lakes and dry land, if the land is not too dry, nor too cold. All animals live parasitically on green plants, which are the only organisms to earn their own living (except possibly some very special types of bacteria).

The stream on the hillside is just a lot of bits of stuff shaking down together by chance, like but smaller than the loose stones of a scree on the hillside. Sunlight shining on bare earth is similar, only the bits are all of molecular dimensions and far too small to see. When a man prepares a special conduit, fits a hydraulic ram and runs part of the stream through it, *he* is not just shaking down, he is *doing* something by choice. The ram then *does* something and by choice, but the man's choice not the ram's. So the green plant *does* something, it is not just shaking down ; we cannot quite say that it *chooses* but we can say that it *acts*, and it has a certain kind of freedom of its own, within its limits, very narrow ones. Its only *act* is to grow, but under different conditions it will grow differently, and if conditions are adverse it can stop growing and die. Taking the earth as a whole in terms of the 2nd Law, dying is the more ' natural' process. Moreover, under the same conditions of environment different species of plant can grow, each one in its own fashion and each equally well. Form of growth depends only in part on conditions, more conspicuously it depends upon the seed from which growth has come ; to that extent the plant is autonomous ; it is not compelled from without. (Cf. Chapter VIII, §5.)

At this rudimentary vegetative level of freedom we can see that there is nothing lawless about freedom ; quite the contrary. Plants impose laws or forms upon material which without them would be lawless or formless ; they are good Aristotelians. At the same time they produce variety, which is lawful, not merely random. There is no breach of physical law ; rather there is use or application of physical law, otherwise running to waste. It is no great exaggeration, if any, to call plant growth a creative act and the beginning of it, germination, the most creative part of it.

In some species of plants most of the seeds (seldom all) germinate freely under very various conditions. Other species produce seeds of which only a few germinate and only under rather special conditions. Both types survive. It is not unreasonable to say (1) that when germination fails the event is ' natural ' and when it occurs is in some way ' supernatural ' or ' miraculous '. Nor is it unreasonable to say (2) that successful germination is ' natural ' and according to law, while failure is an ' accident '. The difference between the two attitudes is that those who hold (1) thank God when their seeds germinate ; those who hold (2) thank themselves for their cleverness or their luck. Contrasted with attitudes (1) and (2) is that of the ' agnostic ' who does not care whether seeds germinate or not.

That is one part of the story. The other is that all living is a perpetual struggle on the part of order against disorder or chance ; a struggle against external physical events, diseases, parasites, enemies of various sorts, and also against irreversible internal bodily processes. Sooner or later, a matter of hours or minutes for smaller organisms, of hundreds of years for forest trees ; but sooner or later the struggle against chance ends in defeat, in death. Under conditions of life on earth there are no victories that do not lead to defeat. This was first pointed out with its physical implications by C. S. Peirce. Poets and prophets have known for centuries that a secular paradise is a fool's paradise ; physical science now confirms them.* The 18th and 19th centuries forgot this ancient wisdom under the impression that they were being scientific.

§4. Unlike the 1st and 2nd, the 3rd and 4th Antinomies cannot be left undecided. The Theses introduce the concepts

---

* *Ecclesiastes*, C. 9., v. 11 : ' . . . the race is not to the swift, nor the battle to the strong . . . but time and chance happeneth to them all '.

of free causation and of God as First Cause. To accept or repudiate these concepts affects our acts and faith. It is just possible for the physicist to claim that he can disregard the issues in his actual work. But the physicist in his spare time is a man like any other and the pretence, that in his laboratory he is not, has worn a bit thin. It is much harder for the biologist to disregard the issues, and I should expect him at least to avoid committing himself to the Antitheses. Some biologists do so commit themselves, probably because they are more nearly 19th century physicists than 20th century biologists. However, no cosmologist or theologian need now be afraid of that pontifical assertion of the 18th and 19th centuries, that God, Freedom and Immortality can all be dismissed as contrary to the laws of physics (or biology or sociology). Marxists may still say it because they still live in the year 1848.

Purely intellectual or theoretical difficulties can always be left undecided, practical or moral difficulties cannot. To postpone a decision about action is itself a decision, and if repeated too often a bad one. In practical or moral terms the two Antitheses stand for indecision and evasion. The Thesis of the 3rd Antinomy means that I can and must choose (within the limits set by circumstances). The 4th, when worked out, means that I can and must choose within the limits set for me by God ; choice becomes both a duty and a right, a reciprocal relation towards and from my fellow men and in the sight of God. The serious challenge to faith in God does not come from theory so much as from practice and specially from political practice. New ' technocrat ' is old tyrant ' writ large ' in new jargon. He is also the Commissar of Arthur Koestler's book, *The Yogi and the Commissar*, but he is not confined to the U.S.S.R. Things would be much easier if he were. He has been known in the West for a long time and he puts on a clerical dog collar when he finds it convenient. It is also unfair to contrast him with the Yogi only, whose religion is more of despair or negation than of redemption.

We must distinguish the technocrat who takes his cue from the superior person of Chapter IX, §2, from the technician and technologist. The technician controls things directly by the work of his hands. He is liable to illusions, as we all are, by mistaking means for ends, but he is necessary and is often, indeed mostly, an honest citizen and honourable man. The technologist, who applies theory to practice, works mainly with paper, a sophisticated instrument, through which more ordinary instruments can be controlled at second hand. He also is needed in the modern world and is frequently an honest citizen and honourable man. Those who control the controllers are unfortunately also needed and far more dangerous. They become technocrats when they get it into their heads that means, operating on a very large scale, are self-justifying and become ends in themselves. Then they also think that with this confusion they have acquired a kind of science for compelling others to do their bidding. Then we get the new magic and witchcraft of the 20th century. Like the old forms it explains away all failures by claiming that more powerful counter magic and witchcraft is at work. Like the old forms too it is powerful so far as people believe in it.

Ancients tyrants, technocrats of sorts in their day, were severely limited by the feeble means available for bullying or deceiving people to do their will, or else exterminating them if they refused. All techniques of ill-government, both genuine and sham, are now far more powerful. Modern urban industrial populations are almost completely at the mercy of any small group who hold the key positions of government. Even rural populations are weaker than they used to be, unless they are so small, so remote, so poor that they are not worth tyrannizing. In the modern world it would be possible for one man to reduce everybody else to a state in which they would have to do exactly as they were told all the time on pain of immediate liquidation. Automatic machines could do the liquidating, as well as most of the administrating now done by human agents. (A really efficient technocrat would dispense with mere bureaucrats, too many of whom are honest and even human.) In such a world there would be no freedom for the rest of mankind except the bare choice between life and death. There would be no criterion of right and wrong except the arbitrary will of the tyrant, which would be arbitrary in the extreme sense that mere whim or chance would govern his decisions. Such a world would be the complete slave state and the complete atheism.*

Initially all would-be technocrats make the excuse that something is wrong and they know how to put it right. Something of course always is wrong, and most wrongs are perfectly genuine, not fanciful at all. What are fanciful are the means for putting them right. In the first place, no man in virtue of superior knowledge or technique is able to tell other people what is good for them, and should not force, threaten, cajole or bribe them into doing it. That is the answer of common sense, known for hundreds of years and ' science ' has altered nothing. In the second place there is the Christian answer, which adds something more and gives the cosmological explanation of what would otherwise be a precarious empirical generalization. Human knowledge, power or will cannot *by itself* turn wrong into right or evil into good. It can do so only through the knowledge, power and will of God. The heaviest indictment that can be brought against the professed followers of Christ is that they have too often succumbed to the temptations which Christ resisted (Matthew 4, 1-11), and followed the way of the technocrat.

No adequate discussion is possible here of the notorious problem of evil, of how to reconcile the existence of evil in the world with the goodness and wisdom of God. Brief comment however cannot be avoided. Evil presents no problem at all to polytheists, idolaters or Manicheans, only to monotheists. The Hebrew view of the problem is to be found in *Isaiah* and the *Book of Job*, the Greek view in the tragic poets, and the Christian view in the Crucifixion and Resurrection of Christ. The Christian view rests upon exemplary fact and not just exemplary story, though if exemplary stories had not already been known and at least partly understood the facts might more easily have been ignored or misunderstood. As it is, the greatest evils provide the clearest indications of how God's creative power operates in the world.

Another problem crops up here which cannot be adequately discussed in this book ; that of Christian evidences. I have

* Plato has said most of this and Professor C. S. Lewis the rest in his Riddell Lectures of 1943, *The Abolition of Man.*

perhaps said all I can in a Pelican Book of 1945 (*Civilization, Science and Religion,* Chapter IV). But the remarks on evidence in Chapter IX, §4, above ought to be applied to this subject in brief. (1) The New Testament texts are earlier and better established than any others that have come down from the ancient world. (2) The discrepancies among the various narratives are less serious than those usually found among ancient texts. (Cf. the radically inconsistent accounts of the teaching of Socrates given by his contemporaries, Plato and Xenophon, not to mention Aristophanes.) The whole trouble has arisen, in spite of (1) and (2) because of (3) the numerous efforts during the past hundred years of scholars, novelists and others to discredit the N.T. accounts of the life, death and resurrection of Christ and to provide more convincing alternative versions. These efforts have been a failure. In the first place, they fail collectively, because they contradict one another and far more radically than anything in the N.T. It is, however, characteristic of the present age to swallow secular camels while straining at spiritual gnats. Alternatives suggested are : (a) that no such person as Jesus Christ ever lived in Palestine, and that he was invented by those who called themselves his disciples ; or (b) that there was such a person but he never made the claims attributed to him, which were invented by the disciples ; or (c) that he made claims knowing them to be false ; or (d) because he was not sane. As to his fate : either (a) after burial his body was taken away and hidden by his disciples (the contemporary anti-Christian version) ; or (β) it was lost by his disciples through inadvertence (a 20th century version) ; or (γ) he was not dead when buried and later recovered, as, presumably, a physically broken man and no help at all to the missionary efforts of his disciples. Whichever you select as true from (a), (b), (c), or (d) and a, β or γ, the others must be false and you need to explain why they are false while yours is true. Worse, you have to explain when, by whom, and under what circumstances the fictitious N.T. version was promulgated so successfully in place of yours. How were the inhabitants of Jerusalem swindled ? I propose, for the benefit of future learned anti-Christians, another version (z) ; that no events occurred in Jerusalem ; that Peter,

[206]

Paul and the other Apostles are all fictitious, and the swindle was promulgated after the fall of Jerusalem in A.D. 70 when it would be more plausible and manageable.

The other main objection is that any of the alternative versions runs counter to the general experience that neither deliberate swindlers nor lunatics suffering delusions produce any large scale enduring effects except death and destruction ; e.g. Caligula, Hitler and the like. Life and constructive effort do not come from such sources. The anti-Christian alternatives to the N.T. deny one simple divine miracle to which all sincere disciples of Christ in all ages bear witness, in favour of a variety of diabolical miracles for the truth of any of which we have to rely on the bare word of an anti-Christian who contradicts other anti-Christians.

There is a kind of political attitude, which I tried to indicate in Chapter IX (§§5 and 6), that can be genuinely scientific in a modest and mainly historical fashion and can preserve the sacramental relation. Sacrament has been misunderstood and misused to produce fantastic and irrational commands and taboos, as in some ancient religions, or turned into trivialities, as by some who profess to be Christians. This has nearly always come of supposing that there are sacred *things*, whereas we know directly only of sacred *relations* for us as men. These were first seen narrowly as between men in the immediate social environment, then more widely, as in the sight of God and men and in the whole human environment. The whole human environment includes the natural resources of the Earth, for which we are God's stewards, to conserve them and distribute the produce fairly. Those who reject the sacramental relation need not bother. Why not waste, exploit and destroy if it pleases us, as it has pleased most people most of the time ? Why bother about posterity ; they do not bother about us ?

The Hebrew view of the sacramental relation is to be found in the concept of God's Covenant, the Greek view in the concept of Natural Law. The consequences of ignoring these ancient insights both by learned and unlearned are now clearly to be seen all round us. To conclude, let me put the matter in Kant's terms, though taking his statements in the reverse order. We are all, as human persons, members of a kingdom of ends. Our first consequent obligation is to respect other persons as members and thus as ends in themselves, never merely as means to our own ends. We can do that most simply, and in accordance with a rule manifest to our reason, by remembering that we ourselves are not privileged, our rights are no more and our duties no less than those of anybody in a comparable situation.

These moral principles are not popular nor ever likely to be. People resent the suggestion that they are dependent beings who do not create themselves. Nor do they care to be told that they are responsible beings whose will, if it is to be moral, must be autonomous and free. Yet they should face the paradox that both statements are true. Those who will not face it can console themselves with the really popular maxim : ' Each for himself and Devil take the hindmost ' and with the really ancient cosmology for which it stands.

APPENDIX

Use and abuse of Visual Experience

This is an attempt to discuss one aspect of the phenomenal world, not to reformulate phenomenalist theory, though that perhaps can be done. It is a brief dogmatic outline without detailed development, qualifications or defence of the many controversial points.

We generally use the terms ' physical ' and ' real ' (also ' objective ', ' genuine ', ' reliable ', ' veridical ', etc.) for whatever is found to preserve constant relations when at least two different lines of evidence or routes of experience are compared. In other words, a physical object occupies a focal region where we are said to find *it* and no other object ; we experience *it* in more than one way, usually through more than one sense ; the different ways confirm or corroborate one another according to rules. Within one sensory field the rules are those of similarity, contiguity and causality, in Hume's restricted sense. Between two sensory fields the rules are of the kind described by Berkeley in his *New Theory of Vision*. All the rules are discovered empirically ; none are *a priori*. At first sight, touch or sound, before corroboration, the cautious observer speaks in terms of ' appearing to be ' or ' looking like ' ; as for instance Macbeth when he doubted whether the visible ' dagger ' was also tangible.

Experience of *touch* in the traditional wide meaning of the term includes the whole exploratory process of handling or dealing with things, as well as being passively pushed or touched. This is pre-eminently the sensory field in which we confirm or corroborate. It is therefore the realm of causal, substantial, mechanical relations (cf. H. H. Price, *Proc. Arist. Soc.*, 1943-44, *Touch and Organic Sensation*). I suggest ' haptic ' experience as a convenient compendious term, emphasizing active grasping and including all processes needed for bodily movement and posture, while excluding organic feeling. One term is needed, in spite of the great variety of receptor and motor organs concerned in any one act of grasping ; indeed because of the great variety as well as our ignorance of their physiology. Corroboration and other kinds of correlation between sensory fields is mainly between visual and haptic, but there are important correlations between haptic and auditory fields, beginning with the effort of uttering sounds and hearing them. Berkeley showed that by interrelating two different senses we build up a system of signs and not a system of causal relations, according to traditional views of causation. Some of the sign relations, not all, seem to be in their own special way necessary, though not *a priori* but empirical. Nor are they logical according to prevailing views about logic. Red things look hot and blue things cold ; the colour is seen as a natural sign not arbitrarily invented, yet not necessary, for some blue things are hot and some red things cold. On the other hand, under normal conditions all cubes both look and feel cubic, and all spheres both look and feel spherical. That rule once found (synthetically established) cannot be unfound (analysed away) and admits of no exceptions. For all that, what is seen and what is grasped are different. (Cf. Molyneux's Question in Locke's *Essay*, II, C. 9, §8 ; Berkeley's *New Theory of Vision*, §132, and *Alciphron*, IV, §§11-15.)

We learn by experience to interpret selected parts of the visual field as objects, which are objective as possessing non-visual characters, experienced or imagined. Excessive reliance on visual imagination and visual language makes us tend to put sight first, not second, and turn the sign into the thing it signifies.

No animal organism could live by visual sense alone, that is just by lights and colours. Colours are a luxury, though aesthetically satisfying, and many animals do without them. Some do without sight altogether. The congenitally blind man is handicapped but nothing like so severely as the congenitally deaf. If he is intelligent he is not badly crippled and can pursue many human activities pretty successfully.

The stable, distinct, firmly outlined pictures of things we claim to see depend to some extent on what is before the eyes at the moment, but to a far larger extent on habit based on previous combined haptic and visual experience, including bodily postures and movements which determine where the eyes are looking, how they do their looking, with what purpose in view (as we say). Visual memory, so far as it is reliable, depends on this combination of haptic and visual, but visual imagination can and does ignore the combinations that have been actually experienced, so that Hume quite correctly accused it of feigning. The most consistent of all visual philosophers (cf. Price, *Proc. Arist. Soc.*, 1943-44,) is also the most percipient. In our visual imaginings we can feign almost anything. Any two-dimensional pattern, or form, or change, or order or disorder is acceptable. Signs operate by no inherent or predetermined order and if habitual order can be ignored, anything may signify anything. Berkeley seems to have known this when he wrote his first book, where he spoke with ' the vulgar ' and called tangibles ' real ' and ' objects ', but visibles just ' signs '.

He could have maintained a phenomenalism of tangibles, and perhaps there are beginnings of this in *De Motu, The Analyst* and parts of *Siris*. The phenomenalism of visibles implicit in his *Principles*, in Hume and many later philosophers looks easy at first sight, but is impossible to work out in detail.

Nothing need be said here on the difficult subject of the internal organisation of the auditory field or its correlation with others, but something more is needed about the correlation of visual and haptic fields. Because visual sense is mainly used as a system of signs for what is non-visual it is illusory in a way that haptic sense is not. There are haptic illusions, but normally they are trivial and inconspicuous. The ' phantom limb ' illusion of those who have had a leg or arm amputated is conspicuous and far from trivial, but is found only in a seriously mutilated organism. Minor illusions of sight are frequent and entirely normal. As against this our instruments of sight are powerful, exact, unrestricted, operate at a distance and with the least possible interference in the field itself. Sight too is used both for synthesis or synopsis (for grasping a whole situation all in one), for analysis (for exactly discriminating parts) and also in the scanning process of looking *round* as well as *at*. Scanning may be a free exploration, or may be tied down to an actual visible route of motion or stable demarcation in the field.

In comparison, haptic instruments are clumsy and limited. They are slow in synthesis and clumsy in analysis. Haptic imagination, if there is such a separate process, can have little freedom but is probably tied down to pre-existing body schemata.* Yet these very restrictions are needed for special functions, making haptic experience automatically and internally self-correcting, little liable to illusion or fiction and genuinely representative.

Visual scanning provides the most intimate link, a real isomorphism (cf. W. Köhler, *The Place of Value in a World of Facts*, 1938, pp. 132 *seq*.) between haptic and visual fields, between hand and eye (cf. Chapters III, §2 and VIII, §2). What the hand draws in outline the eye follows in outline. There may well be some body schema relating the two, just as there may be for what the voice utters and the ear hears. In these relations lies the basic mechanism for symbolism in speech and writing (or drawing). Moreover, we begin our education as babies by handling and exploring our own body surface. By contrasting the double contact of *body surface* with the single contact of *external* objects and the non-contact of

* Cf. W. Russell Brain, *Mind, Perception and Science*, 1951, specially Chapters I and II; also F. C. Bartlett, *Remembering*, 1950. These authors give references to other recent work and the original Kantian conception of schemata.

internal organic feeling we learn to make our basic cosmological distinctions. Sight alone, if we had it, could provide no such distinctions ; its function is to fill out, extend and anticipate an exploration of the external environment that begins and ends with haptic experience. Hearing comes in too with functions similar to those of sight, but through the medium of speech also marks out the realm of *other persons* from that of *other things*. All this is simple and obvious and would hardly need to be said, but for the philosophical chaos created by visualists.

The process of imagining has two aspects, good and bad. It may be mere feigning, the road to fraud or lunacy. If this were all, the old rationalists would be right, and we should have to try to use pure reason without imagination ; an impossible task. The musical composer cannot succeed without using his reason to impose discipline upon his imagination, but without imagination there would be nothing to impose discipline on. His imagination must be auditory in the first place but need not be purely auditory. If I may be allowed to use a much abused word, imagination has a *creative* task. Plato knew this but refused to admit it openly, because of his dread of the fraudulent aspect of imagination, and specially visual imagination. Let us forget this and consider for a moment the favourable aspect.

The constructive (a more modest word than ' creative ') aspect of imagination is the field of operation of the æsthetic impulses, the æsthetic judgment, and the disinterested pleasure that goes with it. The pleasure is not itself the criterion of judgment and there is no justification for the common view that æsthetic judgment is more specially subjective than any other kind of judgment. Even if pleasure were the sole criterion, a disinterested pleasure could produce a disinterested judgment, while a self-interested reason can produce a self-interested judgment and often does.

There might be purely haptic imagination, some kind of play-acting, with pleasure and æsthetic judgment to correspond. It would be purely self-centred, self-interested, thus subjective in the worst sense. But it might also operate in accordance with canons of technical or scientific judgment or if you prefer, canons of reason. More probably we have no purely haptic imagination, which may be just as well. Ordinary imagination is mixed ; visual or auditory at the top, haptic below, unnoticed.

In contrast to haptic experience, visual and auditory are less self-centred, can be almost completely disinterested, and their imaginings may be assumed to correspond. Lastly, why should not æsthetic judgment be able to attain the greatest possible objectivity? Is it not concerned with trying to apprehend the world as God meant it to be, not with snatching, destroying or exploiting?

Now let us apply these general considerations to scientific theories. Those of the basic, classical physical sciences, excluding astronomy, I shall refer to as Group A. They come from correlating the techniques of the drawing board with those of the workshop, a geometry largely visual with a mechanics which need not be visual at all. Geometry without mechanics is useless, mechanics without geometry unintelligible. To correlate the two calls for a process of translation, of linguistic and also non-linguistic symbols (cf. Chapter III, specially §6). Without criteria of equivalence or at least similarity, translation may go wrong. What we do and see bi-dimensionally on the drawing board on an assumed Euclidean plane surface, we can interpret in different ways. We are not guaranteed, prior to experience, any one tri-dimensional equivalent to be acted upon and react; nor, even after experience, that our habitual interpretations are universally adequate or exact.

I suggest that one of the faults of modern architects is that they only look and only at their drawing boards, and these are their idols, in Bacon's sense. They have never constructed a building themselves nor lived in one of their designing.

The basic physical theories of Group A are, as has been said, correlations of the techniques of drawing board and workshop, but they are confined to the man-sized scale of objects. This may be taken as extending from a millimetre to a kilometre, with prolongations by special devices a thousandfold on either side. Given some more special devices on the large side we enter the province of group B, the macroscopic theories of astronomy. On the small side are the theories of Group C, on molecular, atomic and electronic scales. These entities are invisible and not ' scopic ' at all, so must not be called ' microscopic ' but ' microhaptic ', for they are actually handled (cf. Chapter VII, §8). Astronomical objects are not yet handled and that is fortunate for human welfare, but it handicaps astronomical theory. Besides these three, there is also Group D, the theories of the organic realm, man-sized and strictly comparable to Group A, in many ways, though not in all. Every organ of a living creature is a machine of a special sort, the parts of the organ are related mechanically and teleologically, i.e. for a function. These organs are related to each other mechanically and teleologically, and as *partes extra partes*, in Leibniz's phrase. No whole organism however is equivalent to a man-made machine, which is quite definitely a part and not a whole at all, for its structure and function are imposed on it from without by human organisms. Most man-made machines are unlike living organisms in being composed of different materials, put together by different means, operating on a different scale of magnitude according to the different rules of that different scale.

To return to Group B ; astronomical observations are used for calculating, after the manner of Aristarchus, the sizes and distances of bodies seen but never handled (cf. Chapter IV, §§4 and 5). The means of observation are : directly by the intervention of the human eye, indirectly by the intervention of a photographic plate, rather more indirectly by radio-telescope. Every measurement calls for mechanical manipulation, but, for astronomy, of instruments alone, so that the mechanics are subordinate and incidental. What has to be determined is an angle of projection of visible or other rays, or else an intensity of light. The results are worked out in terms of Euclidean projective geometry, for which two postulates are required. They may be put roughly as : (1) All parts of space are alike (cf. Chapter X, §2). (2) Figures of any magnitude may be similar, e.g. the sum of the angles of *any* triangle is the same however large or small the triangle (cf. Chapter III, §3). Let us add another postulate : (3) All physical processes at all epochs of time are subject to the same laws, or all parts of time are alike.

It will be seen that these are convenient simplifications, which we would always assume and use if we could, and can use over limited ranges without serious error. They do not look too good as universal axioms and are not the kind of thing that any cautious man would try to prove. Moreover we should leave room for (4) Principles of Mechanical Similarity, which are awarded capitals because they have some kind of necessity about them. They cut across (2) in a curious way. They may be stated negatively as : Two-dimensional models of different magnitudes may be similar, but their three-dimensional mechanical counterparts are dissimilar, statically and dynamically. (C. Chap. VIII, §5 and D'Arcy Thompson, *Growth and Form*, 1917 and 1948.)

To return to astronomy ; Einstein's theory of relativity rejects postulate (1) in any complete form, except (axiomatically) for empty space. By now, however, there is a strong suspicion that no space is quite empty ; i.e. space between stars in our galaxy contains gas (at very low pressure), dust and larger solid particles (at very low mean density), but definitely not nothing. Space between galaxies may be much the same. This is good news for Descartes, but for Einstein not so good, as it makes his exception of doubtful significance. However that may be, the astronomer, when he is determining sizes and distances must adhere strictly to the Euclidean postulates (1) and (2) or else abandon his efforts. Whitehead objected to Einstein's rejection of (1) as abolishing universal laws of nature in favour of local approximate laws varying according to the mean density of matter in the neighbourhood. Yet Whitehead himself rejected (3), also abolishing universal laws of nature in favour of changing temporary laws. It must be said in defence of Whitehead that faith in (3) calls for greater credulity than faith in (1).

The astronomer who accepts all three postulates interprets the ' red shift ' of the spectral lines of the more distant galaxies as a Doppler Effect, i.e. as showing that the galaxies are receding from the observer and the more distant they are, or the fainter their light, the faster. The sole available evidence is this single correlation, the fainter light is redder. We can, however, also say with complete confidence that the fainter light has travelled farther, been a longer time on the way and is older. It is not absurd to suppose that long ago atomic machinery worked slower and produced redder light in the process, nor yet that the wave length of light might get a little longer on a very long journey. These are two uncorroborated hypotheses ; that of regression is a third, equally uncorroborated. No one either supports or contradicts any other ; any one may be true or false, all may be true or false.

Astronomical evidence when pushed to the limit is handicapped in various ways discussed in Chapters IX, §4 and X, §2. I must now make the further comment that astronomical evidence is entirely optical and cannot be directly corroborated by haptic evidence, as can any optical evidence used for the theories of Group A. In fact the experimental sciences should be considered as primarily haptic, but supported by visual observation.

Now what about the microhaptic theories of Group C ? They have flourished in the last century and a half with the development of techniques for handling things by indirect control on a scale which is large enough to be practicable for human hand and eye, but small enough and discriminatory enough to bring out discontinuities, where they are to be found, and contrast them with continuities. In the 1800's Dalton produced evidence of discontinuities in chemical combination which established the chemical atomic theory (cf. Chap. VII, §8). Almost simultaneously Thomas Young displayed effectively (with very simple techniques that Newton could have used had it occurred to him) the semi-continuous, semi-discontinuous or periodic character of light.

Together these two gave us the beginning of microhaptic practice and theory. Later came the three-dimensional geometry of carbon compounds, and the refined development of the kinetic theory of gases, already present in a crude form in Dalton's theory. The 20th century brought J. B. Perrin's beautiful demonstration that the kinetic theory of gases can be applied to particles visible under the microscope and displaying Brownian movement (*Les Atomes*, 1913). Then came the equally beautiful demonstration by the Langmuir trough technique of sizes and shapes of certain organic molecules spread on a water surface (N. K. Adam, *The Physics and Chemistry of Surfaces*, 1941). I shall not describe here the better known quantum theory of light or theories of sub-atomic particles. None of all this practice and theory needs to be taken visually, nor should it be taken so except as a metaphorical short cut. These short cuts fit into our ordinary habits and ordinary language so well that they cannot be abandoned. They have led to superstitions of many kinds ; they need not do so, provided they are cautiously and properly interpreted. My final remarks are intended to indicate the kind of caution to be used.

The ' Billiard Ball ' theory of the physical universe flourished throughout the second half of the 19th century, when every gentleman owned a billiard table and even those who were not gentlemen played billiards. The surprising thing about it is not that it has been almost forgotten, but that it worked as well as it did (cf. Mary B. Hesse, *Science and Human Imagination*, 1954, specially Chapter III). The properties of billiard balls are peculiar to a limited size range and a very limited range of materials. For instance bodies as big as the earth or the moon would not display them. Spherical bodies composed of sugar (e.g. boiled sweets) would not display them for they would stick together on impact or break up or both. There was no good empirical argument for supposing that very small bodies would behave like billiard balls. So far as their behaviour can now be described in detail it is clear that in many ways they behave differently. If gas molecules ' touch ' each other they almost certainly stick together like damp sweets ; if they ' bounce off ' (as in a perfect gas) it is because they have not ' touched '.

The main defect of 19th century theorists was that of David Hume, they preferred to look on at games of billiards. They were imagining or drawing what billiard balls looked like on the table, not what the man holding the cue is *doing* with one, nor yet what the moving balls are *doing*. This visualist foible may do no harm in certain cases when you may safely neglect differences caused by change of scale or of other mechanical conditions.

For the purpose of working out the dynamics of (say) gases what happens at the time and place of interaction (contact or near contact) is important ; what, if anything, happens in between is not. Provided that ' molecules ' occasionally interact as distinct units they might have no separate existence in the spaces and intervals between. The visualist, specially the ink and paper visualist, forgets this possibility because his marks on paper are permanent or nearly so, as are the billiard balls. He assumes that any ' real ' entity is like them, unchanging, recognizable, self-identical. Consider now some cases where the visualist assumption is less plausible than it is for gas molecules.

(1) Experimentally the quantum of light makes its presence felt (not directly seen) when light is emitted from a body into space or absorbed by a body. It appears in a process of transmission, at the place and time of transmission and not at other places or times. In this it is comparable to the gas molecule which manifests its discreteness in ' collision '. Nobody, however, supposes that permanent, discrete light quanta travel through (nearly) empty space.

(2) The Daltonian atom manifests its singularity and discreteness in chemical combinations and decompositions and then only, with one important exception. By X-ray analysis crystals display a regular spatial pattern centred on the atoms of the crystal. In the crystal there may be no sign of chemical molecules, of separate groups of atoms in constant numerical proportions. Molecules are discovered in gases, from their mutual collisions and collisions with the walls of containers, which are registered as gas pressure. The molecule H_2O is found in steam but not in ice. It is necessary to add that liquid solutions also display certain gaslike properties in which osmotic pressure takes the place of gas pressure. Thus molecular characters can be observed in solutions by suitable methods.

(3) Light quanta, chemical atoms, molecules all make their appearance in transmission, interaction, collision ; in some dynamic process which is singular and discrete, occurring at a time and a place under special conditions and not at intervening times and places. They are not discovered as permanent states. These considerations can be applied to sub-atomic particles by those who are more competent than I.

There are interesting biological parallels that may be mentioned as they are perhaps less familiar and cause more confusion.

(4) Impulses are transmitted along the fibres of nerves and muscles according to the All or None Principle, that is to say in

quanta or packets so that there are always one, two, three or some other whole number and never fractions of them. It is only what is transmitted that displays this 'atomic' character. The initiating process in (say) a motor nerve cell is itself continuous and capable of more or less, but what is transmitted is not. It is rather as if the separate bullets fired by a machine gun were not fired by separate explosions, one for each bullet, but by continuously maintained pressure in the chamber.

An interesting large scale model of the nerve impulse was studied by the late Professor Lillie in the 1920's.* A wire of soft iron immersed in nitric acid of suitable strength becomes coated with a resistant film of oxide ; a scratch or an electric current at one end will cause a brief chemical reaction, which then sweeps down the whole length as an 'impulse'. After a short interval (refractory period) another 'impulse' can be produced in the same way. Many features of the iron wire process are closely analogous to those of the nervous process. At the time, some of the more feather-headed scientists said that it would be possible to find out all about nerve processes by the easier method of examining iron wires, because the wires gave them something to visualize. Of course it was not so, and Lillie himself was not deceived, but took care to point out differences as well as similarities. The differences belong to the different scales of the structures involved and different chemical reactions. Of the resemblances only one need be mentioned ; both processes are of the nature of a single wave, which is either complete or absent, for both consist of chemical reactions which, once initiated, run to completion and liberate energy. Such processes occur in many types of structure on any multimolecular scale of magnitude. Again, what is singular, discrete or atomic is a process of transmission, not a structure.

(5) There are unitary or 'atomic' processes, the genes of the geneticist, involved at certain stages in the transmission of hereditary characters of all living organisms, except perhaps the very lowest. The material that is transferred from one cell nucleus to another (at ordinary mitotic division, at the reduction division to form gametes which have just half the nuclear material, at conjugation when two gametes form a fertilized egg cell) must be in packets, single and separate. In the intervals between cell divisions, what is at work in the nucleus controlling growth processes need not be in single or separate packets. Many geneticists imagine the genes

* R. S. Lillie, *Protoplasmic Action and Nervous Action*, 1923. A. V. Hill, *Chemical Wave Transmission in Nerve*, 1929. A. D. Ritchie, *The All or None Principle*, 1932, *Biological Reviews, Vol.* 7, *p. 336.*

as like billiard balls or dots on paper, and equally permanent. There is no evidence in favour of such a view and a good deal against it.

These remarks are intended to bring together a number of points about the perceptual status of scientific theories, otherwise obscurely scattered through the book. Incidentally they may reinforce the argument of Chapter X, that there is no purely physical cosmology.

BIBLIOGRAPHICAL NOTE

As the reader may have discovered, I believe that special studies of special subjects and above all of how particular persons have dealt with particular problems are more significant for the history of science than comprehensive surveys, which are bound to obliterate details. For this reason I have quoted and used extensively the work of Heath on Euclid, Aristarchus and Archimedes. Several other studies are quoted also. Here I append a short list of recent works not quoted, but eminently useful.

Louis Chauvois, *William Harvey*, Eng. trans. 1957. A sympathetic portrait of the man and his times, as well as an excellent account of his work.

Sir Harold Spencer Jones, *Copernicus*, The Selby Lecture, 1943, (University of Wales Press). Clear, concise, yet states all essentials ; a model exposition.

L. T. MORE, *Isaac Newton*, 1934. Careful and judicious.

C. E. Raven, *John Ray*, 1942. Portait of a remarkable man and pioneer naturalist.

Alexander Wood, *Thomas Young*, 1954. Young is outstanding, even in the early 19th century, as one who made fundamental discoveries with the simplest of means and in many fields.

Lastly, everybody ought to read what Charles Darwin *wrote* : the *Origin of Species*, of course, but also *The Voyage of the Beagle*, and the *Autobiography*, now available in full, edited by Nora Barlow (1958). Most of what has been *written about* Darwin can be left unread.

On the philosophical side I append a list of those recent books, known to me, which discuss the problems and do not evade them. Some are referred to in the text above, but for convenience are listed here and in chronological order.

1920, A. N. Whitehead, *The Concept of Nature*. Further references to Whitehead would have to include all his philosophical works.

1924, N. Kemp Smith, *Prolegomena to an Idealist Theory of Knowledge*. In the Preface the title is expanded with the words ' on realist lines '.

1938, W. Köhler, *The Place of Values in a World of Facts*. A difficult book. His Gifford Lectures, when published, will both clarify and expand the thought of this earlier work.

1939, John Macmurray, *The Boundaries of Science.*

1945, R. S. Lillie, *General Biology and Philosophy of Organism.*

1950, Agnes Arber, *Natural Philosophy of Plant Form.*

1954, Agnes Arber, *The Mind and the Eye.*

1958, M. Polanyi, *Personal Knowledge*. This appeared after these pages were in print. I am glad that I can now acknowledge my debt to Professor Polanyi for the stimulus I have received in the past and refer the reader to this systematic exposition of his thought.

INDEX

The principal references are indicated in bold type.

Index

PRINTED IN GREAT BRITAIN BY OLIVER AND BOYD LTD., EDINBURGH